DUNES REVIEW

COVER IMAGE : *Turbulence Over Orange* by Kaz McCue. Photograph. Image courtesy of the artist.

DUNES REVIEW

VOLUME 26 ISSUE 1

SUMMER 2022

CONTENTS

Land Acknowledgement

Dunes Review is published on the traditional lands of the Grand Traverse Band of Ottawa and Chippewa Indians. It is important to understand the long-standing history that has brought us to reside on the land, and to seek to understand our place within that history. We thank the Anishinaabe people for allowing us to be here today.

Cover Artist's Statement

Water is the most abundant compound on earth and can be seen as a liquid, a solid or a gas. Throughout time, humans have had an intense attraction to and relationship with water. Water is an important component of our physical existence but it also represents much more than simple sustenance. Water lives in psychological, emotional, spiritual, and intellectual aspects of our lives as well. As I have explored my own relationship with water in visual terms, I also have realized how deeply connected my life is to water. When I was young, my family spent summers at the ocean and I used to play in the creek that flowed through our property. My zodiac sign is cancer, a water sign. I vividly remember the physics lab exercises that dealt with wavelengths by creating ripples in water. Water can be incredibly soothing and comforting but it can also be terribly destructive. While all of these factors are important it is the dynamics of water to which I am really becoming attracted. I began to see a direct correlation between the water I was using as a subject and the technology I was using to capture it. With a camera, you can record a duration of time in a single frame or stop the action with a fast shutter speed. As the camera exaggerates any sense of time and action, water can also vary its visual presence based on its flow or stagnation. It is the diversity of this dynamic in which I am most interested.

In the course of pursuing the landscape as a photographic subject, I became more and more entranced by water and what it was capable of doing visually. After a while, the landscape disappeared and only the water was left. The images you see presented here were created during a three-month residency at the Prairie Center of the Arts in Peoria, Illinois. My goal for this residency was to take what I knew about water, light, and photography into the studio in order to create a controlled environment where I could manipulate all three of the elements in the creation of abstract images. To me, these photographs are more like paintings and drawings and speak to an emotional landscape where water is not only the subject but also the tool for creating images.

—Kaz Mccue

Editors' Notes

This issue's cover is Kaz McCue's photograph Turbulence Over Orange. We chose the image before we knew its title, but the idea of turbulence resonates. It seems to be everywhere—in national and international violence, in uncertainties of all kinds, and in what seems to be a new habit around our town: drivers making aggressive left turns just as the light changes, in the face of oncoming traffic, while flipping a middle finger to the world at large. Wait, what? Can't we count on anything anymore? There is also disquiet in the selections in this issue. Disquiet and many concerns about different kinds of safety. Kaz McCue writes that he's interested in the dynamic of water, its flow, its movement, its range of possibilities. In the writing here, I'm struck by the range of responses to relationship, to difficulty and danger, and the many ways people do our best, working without a metaphorical safety net, trying to move towards good. As always, I'm grateful for the writers out there working to share some truth with us. I hope you find some inspiration in these voices.

— Teresa Scollon

Fog: it can obscure turbulence, meaning we can't see what's about to hit us— or it can be what encompasses us when we ourselves are tossed about. In this issue, both physical and metaphorical fog take their toll. When we can't see what's up ahead, and when we can't see where we are in the midst of the world's chaos, it can be difficult to parse memory from fiction.

The past is a story we tell ourselves / however we can, says Dina Folgia. Yet the language we choose for those stories often betrays us, as Romana Iorga explores: *language has broken all her promises.* What carries clear meaning for us can be understood differently by others. *My understanding is a fistful of fog,* writes Ann Weil, *a mirror of mist that will not clear.*

So what, then, can we do? When we're enveloped by grey mist, when the sky is heavy with threat, when all the world runs amok and we're bereft on a sandy shore? I'll trek with Jennifer Bird to Les Chenaux, *become lake, become sparkle, [hoist] my thousand flags of sun.*

—Jennifer Yeatts

1

Richard Hoffman
SETTLER

       Behind the cab's tinted safety shield the human operator
   works levers and foot pedals, driving the machine forward
again and again into the home of two parents, three kids, and
an aunt who speak the wrong tongue, read the wrong book,
     have the wrong ancestor. And every time the yellow machine
       backs up it beeps, repeatedly, loudly, so no one will get hurt.

Linda Nemec Foster
THE CEMETERIES
NEAR THE UKRAINIAN BORDER

The dead are orthodox. They want cut flowers arranged in perfect
bouquets above their hearts and freshly starched bows of white
linen attached to their gravestones. Even the mourners have to
pay attention to protocol. Heads must be covered, hands folded
in prayer, no distracted gazes to the right or the left. The dead are
always in your face, up close and personal. "Don't you dare forget
us," they demand. And the old women near the Ukrainian border
never do. On market day they buy extra bread then cross the San
River to the cemeteries. They cover their gray hair, anticipate
rain. Toss small crumbs filled with rye and poppy seed amidst the
crowded crosses, the rusting crucifixes nailed to trees. They watch
the blackbirds take the bread to heaven and pray that the dead will
get fat and be satisfied.

Joseph Hardy
I DROVE BY

and could not own the rage,
but imagined the weight of a heavy pipe

swung like an axe in the dark,
and thought, how many blows would I need

to shatter a bus-stop-shelter like that, and how
could anyone carry such a weapon unremarked.

It wasn't one bus stop that summer.
Sprays of pebbled glass glittered on sidewalks

on different blocks of that route for weeks.
Caught my eye in my commute, not letting it pass

as it did over the tired women, sitting,
rested bags between work shoes.

I confess I did nothing with those feelings
that summer but buy a mirror

from a local artist, who'd stopped her car
hurriedly, ahead of city maintenance

and swept a pile of the glass into a cardboard box
kept for art supplies in her trunk.

Imagine thick sea-green fragments, set deep
in red adobe, around a mirror's reflection

and you might see how it could hold violence.
The way a trashcan later that summer was held

suspended in air, half-way
through a broken bus stop wall.

Joy Gaines-Friedler
PICKING UP THE PIECES

CAPE CANAVERAL, Florida (Reuters). *A [six-tones] NASA science satellite pierced the atmosphere over the Pacific Ocean and fell back to Earth, the U.S. space agency said on Saturday, but it was not yet known where the remains landed.*

Morning. Through the window a low pitch of light.
Across the street, the outline of elms emerge

like the slow knowing of love. But then you
second guess yourself. Scotch glasses

hold last night's good stories, jokes
you won't remember — secrets.

I'm reading that an aged satellite finally shattered its way to earth.
The report reads "six tones" instead of tons "pierced the atmosphere."

I imagine people in Calgary hearing blurry
indistinct sound, notes separated by whole-steps dissonance,

like a choir gone bad; I imagine Calgarians unsure
whether to stand in the fascination of mysterious sound,
                                    or run inside, take cover.

Already the sky has brightened, the trees less enigmatic.
That nothing lasts long is an understatement.

I'm thinking, even with today's technology a humpty-dumpty satellite
can't be put back together again - that last night's beguiling details
            will soon be scattered somewhere in memory's wreckage —

I prefer to imagine a satellite, singing its way to earth,
not as an ending, or a kind of broken promise

but rather, the cosmos asking us to take notice,
to notice the way the present owes a debt to the past.

The sky holds a flash of sunlight. The wind's picked up.
There is a sound floating through the trees
like space debris.

Will Stiefel
SIDE SPLASH

I was ten when my dad picked me up from school and told me I
was never going back. His truck idled loudly out front, begging
other students to stare before locking themselves in their sleek
minivans. Nothing new. Except his copilot was missing and had
been for almost a week. Her lavender and sage still wafted from
the passenger seat window, mixed with his tobacco. But his eyes
were raw and frantic, searching for something, not looking at me. I
stepped into the cab and sat in my mom's empty seat.

"It's your seat from now on, Big Man." Big Man, that's what
he called me when he knew I was scared. Time to buck up, Big Man.

A plastic jar full of gum sat in the cupholder next to a bottle
of Gatorade. The liquid inside was cut apart, like oil and water; the
darker bottom buffered a floater of something distilled.

"You ready for an adventure?" He took a sip and cringed
only a little, so I wouldn't notice. Not long after, he would hardly
cringe at all, and I would hardly notice anymore.

"Where are we going?" I asked.

"We're going where your mom would go. Now shut that
door hard."

We drove all night from Boulder heading west. Endless
black switchbacks loomed just beyond the headlights' reach. When
I woke, we were parked at a rest stop in the desert somewhere near
Grand Junction. Soon we'd reach Utah. I wondered how long
it'd be until we set foot in Colorado again. My dad snored behind
the wheel with his baseball cap pulled over his face. He looked
peaceful. Lines of dried saltwater crusted down from his eyes to his
cheeks, settling into his dark beard. The Gatorade bottle was empty.
I picked out a mint, opened the door, and walked into the cold
desert. He'd still be there in the morning. I'd be sure to get back
in time to make us some breakfast before we headed on. He loved
when I got our bulky propane stove going early.

We overlanded through the west, and I began to wonder where
exactly it was my mom would go. Maybe it wasn't just one place.
My dad had thrown a camper on top of the pickup and he fit it
with everything we'd ever need, except money. The whole place felt

like a fort we built together. It mostly smelled like him—patchouli and tobacco and stale beer. The good kind of tobacco though, the same kind that stained his fingernails. He wouldn't let me burn sage like my mom used to, but we still dried lavender out under the windshield whenever I brought a bundle back. He needed someone to help out and I made sure to stay useful. We had an unspoken respect for one another, I assumed, especially because he rarely spoke.

Some rituals stayed; some were phased out. Most mornings began with sizzling sausage and fresh, chocolatey coffee. We'd sit hidden in the camper while the sun came up, him staring out the window, hand-grinding enough beans for a full thermos and small camp mug for me. I'd get a half-caf—half coffee, half hot water—with a little leftover half-and-half we'd pocket from unchaperoned gas stations. We did a lot of petty pilfering from gas stations. After every successful mission, we'd celebrate our loot—candy bars, cigarettes, maybe some beer—and Dad would ruffle my hair or even flash a smile. His routine made sense to me in the primal way starting a fire makes sense. We'd silently go about our business eating breakfast, drinking coffee, him rolling tobacco from a pouch of American Spirit. I never smoked. But I knew always to get the dark, never light blue.

He'd ask me about my dreams and I would slowly unwind what transpired in my subconscious. His eyes stared off beyond mine, listening intently for something else. Sometimes he'd nod in what I thought was approval. Other times he'd shake his head, frustrated. He wanted to hear something from my mom, anything. When I met her in a dream, it would be as if I was waking. I couldn't move, but I could watch her as she moved into a muddy clearing surrounded by trees. I tried to yell, but my voice was muffled. I'd push until my fear and desperation climaxed a shallow moan. That noise could break through to reality, where my dad would be waiting, holding me, staring.

"Help," I'd whisper.

"All right now, it's all over with," he'd say, his eyes as glassy as mine.

"Where'd she go?"

"Still here somewhere, playing hard to get is all. Harder than ever."

8

He would hand me a notebook full of other dreams and tell me to write down everything, as if I would forget. I'd describe how the lights turned on when the sky reached down to silence her.

I continued to follow, watch, and wait on his every word. I felt like an accessory, a part of his camper. Put the boy outside to play, feed the boy. I thought our life was as normal as everyone else's. So I kept following and he kept leading, from Colorado to Utah, to hiding deep in the Pacific Northwest. Winter rolled in cold and damp. The forest turned emerald and the mountains became greener than any faraway jungle I had read about. The thick, verdant forests seemed to calm my father's shaky hands.

"Look at this," he said, waking me up deep in Douglas fir country one morning. The sky was obscured by a thick cloud of fog that hung low enough you could touch its wetness. Spongy, space-neon moss coated the tree bark facing north. He held a piece up for me to touch.

"You ever seen something so cosmic?"

"Mom used to say we move too much to grow any green."
I stroked the velvet chunk of earth and thought of her buried deep beneath it.

He looked back at me and a smile broke through the fog in his eyes. He stood up.

"C'mon, I'm making breakfast, then we'll see what else is out there."

He made the best breakfasts, those rare mornings when his sober hands remembered how to steady themselves.

He liked that I had my mom's hands. They were made for climbing rocks: the fingers thicker than most kids', well-seasoned with calluses. My mom spent years guiding me up granite walls and showing me how to map my way across boulders. She pushed me further and further until it got to the point I could scramble around all day before coming down. But I only ever climbed alone after my dad took us on the road. He didn't have the patience to sit and belay me.

When we moved south to set up camp in California, I spent nearly every hour of daylight, and a good bit of moonlight, studying the steep walls surrounding us. My hands and feet learned how to follow the chalk marks left snaking up each route. And I remembered my mother's words whenever I found myself unable to keep them moving, frozen with a fear that came flowing from somewhere unknown.

"Look up," she'd say. "Everything you need is right in front of you."

But it wasn't always that easy. Near the end of the season, halfway up a route, I saw thick clouds begin to pour into the valley tucked thousands of feet below. I'd seen clouds move that swiftly before. I knew what could happen if they wrapped you up high on a mountain.

I focused my attention on each hold, fixing my fingers over the small crimping edges that ran up the route. I reached down to dip my hand in powdery chalk. I was already too far up the rock face to climb down and there was no rope to repel. But I trusted my hands to finish the route. My body flexed and pulled skyward faster as the air around me grew thicker until the sun disappeared and distant thunder announced its arrival.

My hands reached over a ledge along the top of the wall and I pulled the rest of my body up and over. A plume of clouds moved swiftly up the ridgeline. The storm was coming faster than I anticipated. My legs instinctively moved downhill and off the back of the peak. I hit the dirt path that led back to my camp and ran as fast as I could. My dad would likely be there, wading in the river's fast-moving water, drinking and fishing in a plea for peace. We both found the escape we wanted when I went off to climb: mine in the high alpine, him in that fluid numbness.

I ripped through the switchbacks, my lungs filling with damp air. Raindrops peppered the pine needles, the storm building until they became a deafening chorus. Darkness was slowly consuming the forest. Then a white flash lit everything back up.

I remembered the first time I ever saw lightning so close. Mom had taken me to climb the Flatirons above Boulder, in the foothills of a mountain range that slowly eased into distant snow-capped cathedrals. The sun was blinding at just over five thousand feet, and it got stronger the higher we climbed. Then there was no sun at all. Only dark thunderheads. They emerged from behind the ridge as if they'd been hiding there the whole time. I felt a wet, charged blanket descend over us. Soon it was as if we were inside the storm, which was still oddly silent.

"Come on, Big Man, don't be scared," my mom coaxed, leading me back down the steep, slippery rock.

"I'm not scared," I called back. Even though it was my first time climbing the route. Not to mention downclimbing in the face of a thunderstorm.

"No, you're not. Nobody's scared in this family, are they?"

"Nope, nobody!"

"Nobody!" She hopped off the rock face and back onto the trail. I hopped off behind her.

On the path back down, the trees were sparse and coverage was limited. I felt the atmosphere holding its breath. I struggled to keep up with her while the rain flooded the dirt path, deafening and painfully heavy. First a flash. Seconds rolled by that seemed like hours. One Mississippi, two Mississippi, three Missi—boom—three miles away, I thought. Or at least that's what she'd taught me about counting lightning. Truth was, it was already too late for counting. The storm moved over the peak and enveloped the valley faster than wildfire.

The strikes came fierce and frequent. Every explosive charge that went off stopped me in my tracks and I gazed upward. My mom would turn back and gently urge me to keep moving downhill.

"It's just God bowling in the clouds!" she'd say. "Must have rolled a gutter. He never could bowl anyway. More cut out for worlds and galaxies." Waving me down, she stood in a clearing just below the tree line.

"Hey wait, I'm hurrying," I pleaded, knowing that, of course, she'd wait for me.

I was desperate to catch her. When you're a child, all you do is play catch up. You follow the leader until you grow tall enough to look them in the eye. I followed her still as she began to sing fearlessly.

"Rain, rain, go away...come on back some other day."

Her body spun around, her long braided hair whipping and spraying and her arms outstretched to the sky, inviting the terror that so consumed me. That song plays on repeat every time I think of her there, surrounded by ancient cottonwoods, turning round and round. Then it stops. And my mom falls to the ground, her shoes smoking and melted.

In a flash, all that infinite electricity traveled through her body and into the earth. It only took a moment for her heart to stop beating. Yet the world kept turning and I kept running and running. I was so far away. Too far away. And I knew nothing of lightning strikes or resuscitation. I only knew the sound of thunder bellowing above as if moaning at its mistake. The smell of soaked earth and petrichor mixed with death. In the end, my father found us and carried my mom down. I followed close behind. I hated that I couldn't carry her then. I've tried to carry him the best I could since.

Thunder cracked again and the memory faded with it. I ran down the mountainside, away from the storm that haunted me. The winding river appeared with our camper tucked into a patch of redwoods nearby. Lightning illuminated the site, but my dad was missing, his lawn chair empty. A few beer cans lay scattered, recognizable but aimless. And I remembered the doctors explaining how my mom got struck by side splash off a nearby tree. The sky's pure, direct energy connected there before hopscotching over to her. Mother Nature both dealt and deflected the blow, frying the tree in the process. I wondered how much death had splashed over to him. If he'd finally had enough of it.

Until another flash, the reckoning strike, and two soaking hands snatching me by the shoulders. They spun me around to face a man who saw his son for the first time since he lost his wife. His eyes were full of lightning, but his face was soft and scared. Red and raw.

"Thank God," he said. "You came back."

Todd Mercer
INTERIOR IMPRESSIONS
WHEN THE SEXTON FALLS

I'll just rest my eyes a minute,
even though I think I'm standing
with a shovel in my hand, and not lying
in bed. Toward the quiet, somehow distinguished
from the elements of regular sleep. Toward the hush.
Here is my wind-up. Whose voices are those
on the wind? Maybe my mother's among them?
They tell me to let it go and make the big move.
I hear waves break toward me
and I guess I'm late to fly.

Deborah Burand
NAVIGATING FOG

For all of our drive north, my father held the steering wheel, and I, his 56-year-old daughter, sat next to him in the front passenger seat. Maps and travel guides littered my lap while empty water bottles and coffee cups rolled under my feet.

This seat and this role, part co-pilot and part garbage collector, were relatively new to me. This is where my mother would sit on our family drives until she, no longer comfortable sitting up straight for long rides, opted for stretching out in the backseat under a light throw, and I took her place next to my father. She had been teaching us, my father now says, showing the two of us how to navigate together as a team while the cancer that invaded her body moved her slowly but inevitably offstage.

The May rain dampened our passage north from Saugatuck to Traverse City, Michigan. It paused just long enough to let us to drive most of the seven miles of the Pierce Stocking Scenic Drive without the distraction of windshield wipers swiping to and fro, cutting the scenery into frames like a spool of unwinding camera film.

This was our first trip to see the Sleeping Bear Dunes. As the car rolled through the scenic drive at 20 miles an hour, my father grew increasingly animated. His hands, no longer at ten and two on the steering wheel, began sweeping toward the landscape around us. "Just look at this," he exclaimed every few minutes, pointing to the forest filled with stands of beech and maple trees and the rich canopy of leaves overhead that turned the drive into a tunnel of green. His running commentary ran from the informative to the awestruck to the spiritual. Then he said, "Your mother would have loved this," and we both grew quiet, newly aware that there was no gentle body resting on the seat behind us.

We left our umbrellas in the car when we reached the scenic drive's ninth outlook. As we shuffled up the dune, a thin layer of rain-dimpled sand, browned to the color of bread crust, broke under each footstep, revealing the drier and whiter sand below the surface. On the boardwalk that topped the dune, we stood with other damp tourists and peered down 400 or so feet into the waters of Lake Michigan that lapped below. The colors of the lake water on this overcast day resembled the shades of a pigeon's breast, gray tones shifting to blue with a slight rim of green denoting its shallower parts.

After we returned to the car and dusted sand from our shoes, my father lowered his voice as if to confide a secret. "Your mother often told me that she loved how I helped her see the nature around her."

"I know, Dad," I replied as I shook still more sand from my shoe. This was my cue, a chance for me to say something like, "And I love it when you help me see nature, too." But I didn't, for I am setting new boundaries in our father-daughter relationship. I won't become a surrogate for my mother. But I fear that, in this line drawing, I am missing chances to let my father know how loved and treasured he is, still.

When I was a little girl of five or six, I started asking my father who he loved most—my mother or me. And he would tell me, "I love you both." Unsatisfied with his answer, I would ask again and again, until finally my father would add, "I love you both the most—but differently." It is that difference that I am trying to locate and hold onto now.

Rain followed us to our Traverse City hotel, but our room, facing Grand Traverse Bay, had a covered patio where we could sit and watch the changing waterscape without feeling even damp. I uncorked a bottle of red wine and watched a deep fog steal our shoreline panorama.

I tried reading the bay view like I would read a painting at a museum, starting in the left high corner and then tracking to the right. But the picture was changing too fast. By the time my eyes returned to the left, the fog had moved, erasing new bits of the waterscape and revealing others. Moored boats appeared and then disappeared. Piers thrusted into the bay and then vanished. Even the beach chairs near the water's edge wobbled in and out of view.

Not only did the fog blanket our vista, so too did it muffle the sounds around us. No bird cries pierced the cloud that was enveloping us. Even the lapping of waves stilled as if the water had receded from the shore.

"Honey, just look at this," my father said, breaking the silence and holding both hands open wide as if to embrace the whole of the shoreline. "Man, oh man. See how the fog is creeping onto the beach? Isn't it beautiful?" He was giving me a second chance, another opportunity to let him show me the wonders of nature.

I nodded my head in agreement. "Beautiful," I echoed.

"This," he continued, "is how I'm experiencing your mother." He gestured to the ghostly outlines of boats that bobbed in the shallows of the foggy bay. I put down my glass of wine and looked at him, but his eyes were still peering into the cloud that now nearly obscured the beach.

"She's here," he said pointing to the bay. "I can't see her, but I know your mother's here. Just like I know those boats are still out there even though I can't see them now."

Alison Swan
WE ARE ALL SHELL-SHOCKED

We missed the flock
of cedar waxwings
that alighted
in the mountain ash
commencing the process
of converting drupes to birds

       the way sun
and snow and songbirds
borrow the spaces
where leaves catch air
without taking off

       the fact that
when they do finally fly
it is once and breathtaking
because they are going
to ground

Nora Neill
THE PEREGRINE FALCONS

I took the elevator up to the top of the parking garage, our own baby bird needed my body's rest, my careful attention to how and where and the length I moved. Kelley took the stairs; her new blue hat shaded her face; her body tight and lean.

In early June the peregrine falcon chicks started to fly, and we went to watch. When we arrived at the prime viewing spot, we met Gail, from the Audubon Society, who set up her white Prius hatchback for sitting with a scope pointed right on the nesting box.

That year there were only three chicks, for the first time.

Mid-March, bloated with grief from a goodbye to our twenty-one year old cat we awaited a repeat ultrasound to see if our embryo would turn to fetus, Kelley showed me the four eggs on the Falcon-cam; the two previous years we had watched four chicks grow, witnessing them tap and push through their shells, pink and fluffy, with big eyes and voices crying out for more flesh from their mother's mid-air catch, likely a pigeon, certainly a bird bigger than them.

Before the humans built and placed the nest box, an unexciting wood hut with a gravel base, Rebecca laid her eggs in the building's gutters, where they rolled to their early demise. But now, usually, four make it to hatch. Before I knew better, I imagined they all launched, left the nest to find a new building in a different city, while their parents cried and called out for them, long after they'd gone. An origin to "empty nest" discovered.

The year our third and only living baby was born, we learned, there was no chick in the fourth egg. When I heard this, I thought one in four. One in four. I was happy for only a false start, as if Rebecca might mourn the losses differently, as if she would mourn them at all and not simply inspect and then chuck the remains, matter of fact, as she may have shrugged a wing when her earlier eggs dropped, thinking, not this year.

Annually, Rebecca, the mother, sits diligently on her eggs and then huddles around her chicks. As the babies grow, predictably in these first few weeks, she moves positions to warm and shield them. Mama bird scans the landscape, and when the babies are tagged by humans, she dive bombs the human helmets. Soon the chicks near the

18

concrete edge of their corner on the tall 5th 3rd bank building, the urban landscape saving the species from extinction, we hope.

A few weeks after my cervical surgery, we went to see the falcon babies learn to fly; it is early in the season. The two boys (only a guess at sex based on size, really, the females bigger) fledge at 35 days, though they typically start to fly 41 days post-hatch. The first chick drifts to the ground, is followed, put in a cat carrier and taken to a rehab facility to learn to fly in safety.

The second boy - Black 64/Blue R - fledges early too, only to be found when he jumped onto Gail's hatchback, and looked down at her through the trunk window. The previous twenty-four hours her guilt rose as she thought she'd lost him, failed to help the falcon baby survive. But then he emerged and flew to a ledge, where he paced and squawked on a narrow four inches that wouldn't allow his parents to feed him. From that spot to another he moved, until safe, a place where his parents could bring him food.

I couldn't tell who's who between the adult birds, co-parenting as they do, but I imagined Rebecca cannot leave her post near Black 64/Blue R. That she swooped by and nudged the young bird to join her in flight.

With our third second trimester underway, my belly a familiar and yet entirely new rounded shape, my shoulders just pink from the early summer sun, I volunteered two short hours to watch the birds, to track, if lost, if they drifted to ground, if they moved to a new location. Through my monocular, I saw the female baby, baby no longer, flap her wings on the ledge, I thought she might leap, and I felt overcome with something like joy. Her roughly three-foot wingspan wide, the underbelly of her wings striped gray and white, her beak a piercing yellow like her mother's. She didn't go. She hopped back into safety for a few more days.

A few days later, when Kelley and I went on our evening walk, I looked down to see a long, thin, translucent white and pink baby bird dead on the sidewalk. My stomach immediately clenched, as I thought about how the chick could be the same size as our baby, maybe even the same color.

As the weeks after that passed, I thought about how our baby was bigger than a mouse, a chipmunk, a dove, a squirrel. By week eighteen, I knew that our baby was both large and tiny, and could feel their flapping wings against me.

Our big front windows weren't clean, but the robin didn't see it anyway. Bang, then onto the ground. The bird shook and we searched the Audubon sight for information on what to do. A woman picked up when she heard the reason for my call on her answering machine. She explained how to proceed and we planned to bring her the bird the next day, if she made it through the night.

Kelley put gloves on to catch the bird. The robin didn't like the shoe box but eventually she stayed in. We added strawberries and grass and planned to keep her in the garage, away from the urban foxes and raccoons. Then, as soon as we thought we safely contained her, we attempted to add water and she pushed free, released into the air and found the fence where she hopped, seemingly fine.

I laughed a nervous, relieved laugh, awed by how hard we tried to help nature, how hard we tried to help something that didn't need our help at all.

Mid-June, finally twenty weeks pregnant, we learn Black 64/Blue R died when he flew into a window. Another young falcon disappeared, scared, flying away from the rooftop where we all perch to watch the birds, released after a stint at rehab. Typically, when they're dropped off, the parents immediately spot them, know who it is and resume parenting. Now, this teenage boy bird gone. I didn't want to visit the birds anymore. I didn't want anymore bad news, anymore fatalities, anymore need for human intervention. I kept asking Kelley if we will ever know where they are, where they moved once they fully fledge, isn't that why they bother banding them? How do they know where to live? How do they find a mate? On the falcon blog, I learned that half of all peregrine falcons die within the first year of life. Is this travesty or miracle?

The next year, in an entirely new lifetime for us all, our baby girl, who once moved her open mouth to my nipple with eyes closed, bird-like in her searching, wears her "baby bird" shirt and three female falcons circle downtown. At least one of them will die before summer ends. This I know. As I sit with my baby, embracing her as she embraces me, I see how I've been consumed, as if a piece of torn pigeon meat, my flesh inside her beak, and it feels good to be swallowed whole.

Joy Gaines-Friedler
BECOME A TREE

for Chico

Go deep into woods. Stand in the sling
of dappled light. Listen to the woody
wisdom of robins work out their chords.
Feel the green breeze blouse over your
skin, the moist heat of community, a society
of saplings and the old stag-heads reaching
for the same sun. Imagine leafing out. Now
imagine holding an almost weightless nest
in the crook of your arm.

Ellen Welcker
THE BIRTHDAY PARTY

I wore clogs and socks to the beach: dumb.

At dusk the blood moon bled, and everyone's hair, also mine, looked red.

I swayed in time with a dad whose skin dripped from a dip in the lake. I brought him a solo cup of grapes. He stood and rocked his sleeping babe, and in my mind, my own arms ached from long past nights of crook-armed sway.

Anne-Marie called it *champagne*. The lake was foggy; opaque, I'd say. *I have never seen water like that,* I'd say. For Anne-Marie, I read "30th Birthday."

And then, Norm—he played the horn—in the band they'd sung, *do the poets know* and I mouthed *no* and thought myself okay.

Norm and I said *hey*, and how the lake tells you things when you linger a while.

It's like the kinglet comes and you know its name, then the blue-grey gnatcatcher, and you know its name, then the loon. You know their names and what they're doing. You say hello, then goodbye and then you say hello again. It's like that, Norm said, and I said, *yeah—*

Like how the tapir's camo shows its worth in changing light. How statuesque the rhino that daily must be searched for; and the ceaselessness of prairie dogs that only seem the same.

It was satisfying, comparing lakes and zoos. The baby's mouth an *o* and sand between his chubby toes. I'd eaten cake and rocked and swayed.

May I never be afraid, said Alice, and Bronwyn touched her hair; said, *the lake is coming up into the air.*

Randy Praay with Jeanne Blum Lesinski
PERCH

When I was a kid, we went fishing on the Saginaw Bay lots of times.
It was just me and Dad that day in 1965 'cause my older brother who
usually went with us was in the Army, stationed in Korea. Dad woke
me up in the dark fog that morning. He was already dressed in the
green workpants and shirt he always wore, and I put on my jeans
and t-shirt and hurried to the kitchen. He made us bacon, eggs, and
fried potatoes for breakfast, so we would have a full belly to carry
us through the morning. For later he made some ground bologna
sandwiches on Spatz white bread, wrapped in waxed paper and
sealed in his metal lunch box to keep them dry.

Dad had a twelve-foot wooden boat with a 3.5 horsepower
Evinrude motor. It was dark gray and heavy and set very low in the
water. Being so low in the water bothered me 'cause it seemed we
only had four to five inches before water would come over the sides.
It could splash into the boat easy if it was windy and the waves were
high, but we'd bail water with two coffee cans we always kept there.
Even though the motor had its work cut out for it—it only went about
five miles an hour, if it wasn't too windy—it got the job done.

The perch bite was on, and my dad was on it. It was all about
the food, and the fun of fishing together, and the food. My family
ate a lot of fish and wild game 'cause we weren't always able to buy
everything we wanted from the grocery store. But we all knew we
were eating good in the neighborhood, better than the kids that lived
round me. My family knew where that food came from, and most
of the time we had a great time together getting it. Dad came from
a family of dairy farmers that was very poor. They'd worked hard
for the little they had, so Dad appreciated everything he had. Along
with whatever they'd raised and grown on their farm, his family had
hunted and fished. That's why hunting and fishing got passed down
to my brothers and me. None of the other kids in the neighborhood
had a dad like ours who took their kids hunting and fishing all the time.

That morning we towed the boat behind Dad's red-and-white
'59 Ford Fairlane. It was one of the newest cars he'd ever had. My

dad loved that car. We launched out of Quanicassee, about twenty miles east of Bay City. That was a favorite spot to launch the boat 'cause it was remote, so there were not many people at the boat launch to deal with. Dad never liked being around crowds of people. Fewer people to see him take a snort of Seagrams 7 and wash it back with a gulp of Geyers beer. I liked Geyers too.

When we launched the boat from the gravel landing, the sun was coming up and starting to burn off the fog. I wiped the sleep out of my eyes and watched. It was beautiful. I loved being with my dad, just me and him on the water. We were heading for the shipping lanes six or seven miles out in Lake Huron. It was a little cool that morning, but as the sun rose up higher in the sky, it warmed up. We only putted along, so it took forever to get out to our fishing spot.

Finally, we got to the shipping lanes where the bigger perch lived. In no time we were pulling perch that were twelve to fourteen inches, some smaller, but we threw them back. We were out there until early in the afternoon, and by then our cooler was almost full of perch.

I watched the weather change. Storms were brewing up and coming across the bay. One of them was heading our way. You could smell the rain in the air as the dark clouds rolled, and my stomach churned too. Dad was in no hurry to leave 'cause we were catching fish like crazy, but soon we had no choice.

Anyone who knows the Saginaw Bay knows that it's a dangerous place to be when a storm hits 'cause it's so shallow. Shallow makes for bigger waves, and the swells got bigger when the wind picked up.

Dad told me, "Old Timer," as he called all of us boys, "pull up the anchor. We gotta go."

I watched the waves rolling under our little boat get bigger and bigger as I pulled up the anchor. They made the anchor seem extra heavy. I turned and saw a look on my father's face I'd never seen before: flush went to white. Dad started the motor and slowly turned the boat round toward shore, miles away. We knew we were in trouble 'cause with the fierce wind, the storm was building fast. The waves started washing up over the back of the boat. I bailed water with the minnow pail since it was bigger than the coffee cans. But I couldn't get ahead.

24

"We can't keep goin' like this. We're taking on too much water," Dad said. "We need to turn the boat round, head into the waves." He looked me in the eyes and said, "I need you to get up and sit on the bow of the boat."

I sat on the front seat by the bow.

"No, I need you to sit on the bow of the boat."

I didn't question my father. His word was law. I sat on the bow of the boat, with my feet dangling over the front of it, holding on tight to the old Buick hood ornament from a car Dad used to have. This is what we tied our anchor rope to. But this time he took the anchor rope and laced it round my hands so I couldn't fall out.

We would putt our way back toward shore until the next big set of swells came on us. Then Dad would have to turn the boat round, pointing the bow at the waves to keep them from swamping us. With my legs wrapped round the bow of the boat, I held on tight, terrified. As we rose up over the gray-brown waves, some of them ten feet high, I looked behind me. In the back of the boat, Dad was steering the motor with one hand, bailing water with the other. He was so much lower than me when we went over the swells, he looked to be twenty feet away. Now it was cold, really cold, and the rain was coming down so hard it felt like bees stinging me all over. I shivered.

"We'll be okay, as long as we don't let the waves swamp us," Dad yelled.

I wasn't so sure.

It was a long, slow trip. It seemed we could only go for a couple minutes toward land before Dad would have to turn the boat against the swells coming our way. After a half hour or so of us turning the boat into the waves and then putting toward shore and doing it over and over again, my fear began to fade. All I knew was that I was with my dad, and he'd never let anything bad happen to me.

Once when we were turning into the swells, I felt calm and realized it was kinda fun to be on the bow, heading face first into these gigantic waves. Helping Dad make sure our boat didn't get swamped and sink made me proud, and I wanted my dad to be proud of me. I began to yell "Yahoooo" as we rode into each swell. I was having fun, but I also wanted to show my father I wasn't afraid. We'd already gone over some forty giant waves, so I knew if we kept doing the same thing, we'd get to shore safe sometime.

It seemed hours before we saw land ahead. Then the color came back to Dad's face, so I knew for sure we'd be okay. When we drove up onto the boat landing, our boat was almost full of water. Dad untied my stiff hands from the hood ornament. Tears were pouring down his face, and I was crying too. He hugged me but never said a word. We just hugged each other.

Then Dad went to the car and pulled out his pint of Seagrams 7 from under the front seat. He tipped it back and gulped about half the bottle. He chased it with a beer. He handed the Seagrams 7 to me. I'd never drank straight whisky before, but around the campfire my dad had sometimes poured it into my Hires root beer. I took a big swig, and it took everything I had not to throw it up.

We loaded up the boat on the trailer, pulled it out of the water, and headed home. It was a very quiet ride from Bay City to Saginaw. Dad finished off the Seagrams 7. In his own roundabout way, he suggested that it might not be a good idea to tell Mom about our day out on the bay. After all, we were just coming home with a cooler full of perch from another good day of fishing.

I knew Mom would've let him have it for staying out too long with bad weather coming on us, so we said nothing about it. Scaling and scaling, we cleaned fish for what seemed like the rest of the day. We put the perch in recycled waxed cardboard milk cartons filled with water and put them in the freezer. No air, no freezer burn.

We kept out enough for a fish fry that night. Mom did it the old-school way. She rolled the perch in flour with a little salt and pepper and fried them in butter in the black iron skillet. They were the best perch I ever ate, along with homemade coleslaw and French fries. We all ate our fill. I could tell Dad was wondering if I was gonna spill the beans at the dinner table, but I'm glad I didn't. My dad was happy, my mom was happy, and I was happy. That's all I cared about.

Heather Cousins
FISH

Vane —
living wind,
current,

curtain, veil
of flesh,
blinds open
and close
on this window

of living glass,
shingled lamp,
lantern
that carries its fat

with no hands
through the night,
torch
made of muscle;

crossed over,
we turn it this way
and that,

watch it gutter
and gasp —

glitter, flash:
a thousand nails,
fingerless,

silk plates,
sewn mail,

shell ribbon,

a pennant
suspended from a pole,

flag snatched
from the underworld.

Kristy Gledhill
SWALLOW

Through beechnut-strewn woods, the river
sidling slow under overhung bends,
a log-jammed murky tea, thick with half-
swallowed stories, wooded banks harboring
heirloom trash heaps, vined embarrassments,
generational junkpiles, far back on the property
as they could get. Shady riverbank shrines
slumping into the leaf fall, rust-riddled,
shotgun-pocked, squirrel-cached, woodchucked.
Geography of the undammed, this river loose
and reckless, taking your console stereo,
raising you a rusted-out quarter panel. Punky
basement stairway, torn out whole,
and the busted ball-peen used to pry it loose —
linoleum layered back to when Uncle Eph
had the red Fairlane. Spring floods sliding
a washing machine over the slicked bank,
dead-weighting mattress, engine block,
dollhouse, toilet toppling into a waterlogged
Chevy full of fused newspapers. The raw
river silting capsized armoires and bathtubs,
hundreds of horseshoes and the horses
they rode in on, baseball bats and all that
high school regret, mucked-up, kudzu-choked
garter-snake havens of high chairs, hayrakes,
hallelujahs and lost faith. Field tiled, swamp
drained and the river doesn't even remember
its own name, stiffened into its bends, oxbows
held to their word now that so much depends
on fencerows, property lines, posterity,
feeding the river what we can't bring
ourselves to swallow.

Stephen Leggett
WATCHING A FLOCK OF STARLINGS ON THE DAY OF AN ECLIPSE

All in one in nervous sweeps
from the roof to the wires

to the small trees and bushes
anxious restless never content

all in one as one in the wind
landing shadowy and off again

no two grains at rest
temporary as smoke

they spill out across the freeway
in an ever so darkening world.

Dina Folgia
EVERYDAY OBJECTS

in art class   we were asked to reconstruct a bike from memory   only to be informed on a

large projector screen how wrong we were   whole spokes missing   unspinnable wheels

attached to structurally impossible bars   I spent my entire lunch hour   in a cold sweat

wondering why it was that I could picture   the sunflare off its   green chrome exterior

feel the rubber of the handlebars roll out   the rockies under my fingers   but still the cramp

of my synapses   couldn't form the whole from any of its parts   I don't believe memory

is trustworthy the same way I don't believe   in buying new chess pieces   when pawns start

to go missing   you are responsible for filling in necessary gaps   no matter how much you

cared for the full set   no matter how gentle you were   with precious and fleeting things

I only remember the way my grandmother spoke   when she was kidding   mirth creeps into

her tone whenever I recall   her in sincerity   she never raised her voice with me but I wish

she had so that I could picture her   in the rage she earned   know the sound of her life's work

I wonder how many marbles   I have tossed down the stairs in my life   and which one I am

remembering when I hear   the clatter of glass onto polished wood   in her weeping house

the past is a story we tell ourselves   however we can   I just want to get the story   right

Kristy Gledhill
BIG ROCK

My cousin Ellen wanted it
for out by the road—something
special at the new place. Dutiful,
capable, John drove the flatbed out,
brought Johnny along with the backhoe,
stood in the field beside it facing
the woodlot, and spit. Nothing

that would show above
the beans, save for the weeds
that ringed it, that big rock had
heaved itself to, embedded
in the field out back of gramma's
house since way before I was big
enough to knock through the plowed
field with dad to visit it. In flat country,
it's funny what'll surface
and draw you to it.

Halfway to the woods, the open
hand of the rock collected more rocks,
cast-off tractor parts, small skeletons,
snakes, chaff—a landmark in rich
miles of bottomland. I once watched
a hawk bearing a squirming rabbit
spiral to its flat top for a feast laid
out under low Michigan clouds.

John and his boy are big men
and Ellen has that sweet way
about her. Hard to say no.
Those two wrestled, pried and dug
for days between chores, trying to
beat the frost. In the end—the rock
twice the size we'd always thought,

edgewise on the cusp of a jagged hole,
exposed like a farmer's pale forehead
in the back pew — John dug deeper,
tipped the rock and buried it clean,
far out of the reach of disc or plow,
for now.

Scott Beal
FLASH AND SHADOW

We're opening presents one by one, a stack of red
wrapped boxes before me, each bound with ribbon that ends
in shimmery curls my mom showed me how to make
by dragging a blade down the ribbon's length,
an open pair of scissors pressed into your thumb,
firmly but not enough to cut, scissors are dangerous,
mustn't run with them lest you trip and jab the point
through your eye into your brain, and you have to tug them
quick so you hear the thrip then release the ribbon
now to bounce like one of Shirley Temple's locks
shorn from her scalp, which is a lot of work to bind a box,
as if there's a miniature Houdini inside, running out of air,
and after sitting through my father putting his ear
to a wristwatch that spilled from the package he'd been shaking,
my aunt stamping out a half-smoked Tareyton and lighting
another, my grandmother oohing over a pair of gold earrings
that catch the light like the teeth of snakes, I should be frenzied
to dig through the paper and destroy the superposition
of the box's contents, to collapse the possibilities
into a single set of baseball cards or roleplaying guidebook
or even a scratchy sweater I'll have to hold up
to my mother's camera throwing its shadow
onto my face, but their skin too is bare and thin
and glints in places where glitter has dusted off the gifts,
and looks easy to shred if anyone's hand even briefly
takes the shape of a talon, so for once I slide a bitten nail
softly beneath a sliver of tape, so that mom laughs
and says *honey, you don't have to worry about saving*
the paper, and now everyone is watching me,
and no one's eyes twinkle like the lights
choking the tree, and I have frozen with a corner of paper
just beginning to unfold in my lap, because if not this,
what can I save?

Lenny Della Rocca
NOCTURNE WITH BEASTS

Eventually, some get out of cars, sometimes with kids
in pajamas. I step out of my house.
They ask how it got here.
Is it a joke, did it escape.
No, one morning I looked out
my window and there
she was, I tell them.
How strange, they say.
Reporters show up
from everywhere.
What's her name, they ask.
She should have a name.
They have a contest, and I get emails
from all over the world,
most of them telling me to call her Antigone.
On Tik Tok and YouTube,
Antigone munches the highest leaves,
kicks up grass, bored
with the neighbors' kids, who taunt her.
They take selfies.
And from her height above their shoulders, she looks down into
their cell phones.
She seems to know she stands out.
Nevertheless, she's determined to be here.
It's a little intimidating,
I swear she smiles. Sometimes late at night
I feel a kind of folk dance inside me.
It's she, on her long legs,
walking around in the sky.
Everyone comes out of their houses.
What is that? Is it music?
After a few weeks friends come and go
like she's almost invisible.
My wife says she saw something on TV
about a guy in Utah who found a tiger on his roof.
Someone at the grocery store said
a widow discovered a kangaroo
in her pool. Eventually, I figure it out.
I know what's going on. It's going
to rain real hard. It's going to rain real hard for a very long time.

Michelle Menting
SOLSTICE DIFFERENTIAL

The coast is closed, the water
too high, so we resign our hike
on crags and walk through lupine

instead. This makes sense: to greet
this inching of night with flowers
of wolves, siblings of peas, legumes

of luck. Inland, humidity holds
so tight: we seal our lips, choose
silence over sieving the air with words.

Why punctuate this reception
with talk? When haze glaums on,
the sun still sets, but we don't see

a minute of it. Experience isn't
the same as witness. And still
we serve as witness to this curtain

of progress, this veil of smog:
the exhaust of all we've made.
Isn't this world supposed to be a cycle

of greeting, of farewell?
We walk, dusk-rind, to welcome
the season, to watch the light stretch

and stretch before it fades.
We embrace the luck of flowers,
howl at a blinded moon. Who knows

how long before we jar this wheel,
before we're stuck, stagnant,
in our own manufactured dark.

Lorelei Bacht
THERE IS NO DEAD OF NIGHT.

The heart of night beats a deep song
around our tent: every reverse hour
chirruped, croaked and ululated.
One insomniac cricket has been
rubbing his flint stone legs for hours:
one, two, one, two – a syncopated tune
rising above the grass to a backdrop
of frogs – disorganised brass band.
Some time past midnight I ran out
of binaural relaxation music, and it is
cold, but the white owl does her best to
lull my drift bones to sleep. Nycto-
phobia: a luxury reserved for roofs,
panic of the house-arrested. In our
gossamer-thin cone of synthetic water-
proof (one hopes), I am busy watching
children like johnnycakes, checking
for pulse, replacing a blanket again,
again. Why do kids kick? Do they not
feel the bite that arises from the soil
below us? The cold of centuries, stacked
and released, an inhospitable column.
What inner flame carries us through
the night? The metabolic warmth,
the mother's hand, the crickets' plaintive
violin – all boats, to dawn.

Ellen Lord
SUMMER HEAT

after Jane Kenyon

the cricket's
hypnotic mantra
settles into me

the night
is humid and dark
humid and dark

then why
does my body vibrate
with thoughts of you

so eager
for this pending storm
this pending storm

Elizabeth Kerlikowske
FIRST MARRIAGE: ECLECTIC

Ghosts in the sturdiness, the durability of each hutch, whose coffee rings kept a diary of absentmindedness. They inhabited our rooms, slept in the ewer that rests in the porcelain basin, rode the back of the mallard decoy from 1870. I knew my mother's things instead of her: dining table and chairs, her dishes: Country Fair. Grandmother clocks and small landscapes I grew up getting lost in, silverware my hands trained around. Crammed in a drawer, a knot of extension cords that cracked when straightened like old spines stretching. Granite on cabinets. World of mismatched lamps and quilts three-quarters complete. We looked needy but we were rich in relics, in those departed place holders, massive charms we dragged around the country because a piano and what it signified was not optional. We rented the house where relatives' couches came to die.

Gillian Haines
LITTLE GIFTS

I arrived home from volunteering at the prison on Wilmot Street and rushed through my house, shedding shoes and bra, through the French doors to the backyard pond. Goldfish darted from subterranean caves, six inches of fluorescent copper with unblinking eyes. They mouthed my fingers, and as their strings of bubbles popped at the water's surface, my tense thoughts—about Ringer's untreated hernia, Earnest's prison gambling debts, and Dodge's comment that he'd never seen a spoon or a plate until he was seven, when he moved to a group home—slowly faded.

Across a tiny circular lawn, my husband napped on a deckchair. Delia, my eleven-year-old daughter, looked up from a book and waved from a branch high in the grapefruit tree above her dad. She never let him far from her sight. I sprinkled fish food as thin as Japanese tengujo paper and wondered how fish slept and whether they dreamed. They made me dreamy. I spent embarrassing amounts of time staring at weightless fish in a rain-fed pond I'd built in the desert. They'd cost me two dollars each at Petco. Two dollars of magic that slowed my breath. A gift.

I glanced up to see Sugar drizzle pee at the base of fenceposts and at key spots along the garden path. Satisfied there had been no recent incursions, she trotted toward me, tail erect, beaming a look that said, *You're only safe because I'm never off-duty.* She had the ego and coloring of an affable polar bear but because she was only a foot tall, I boosted her to the raised pond's stone rim.

"The goldfish think I'm a God," I confided, reaching for confidence I didn't have.

Her reply was to drape herself along the row of pink capstones with as much languor and grace as Marlene Dietrich.

"Really," I said, enjoying the fantasy. "They look up through the forest of lily stalks and the layers of water and I'm backlit by heaven. I dispense manna."

Whenever I spoke, Sugar's eyes never left my face. The attention I craved. The same attention I gave to the prisoners and my brain-injured husband. Perhaps Sugar could see an Aussie beach girl, a researcher, someone who'd traveled to Myanmar and the Atacama Desert instead of a caregiver landlocked in America and afraid to drive beyond a fifteen-minute radius from a hospital in case Jon had a seizure.

Delia shimmied down the tree, snagging her pale blue tee imprinted with my cartoon of Sugar's face. Sugar was her dog. We'd bought her, sight unseen, through a newspaper ad, and the breeder warned, "Don't you want to see her? She's the runt." But Delia didn't care what Sugar looked like.

Delia smiled at me as she walked to the pond, gathering chew toys, balls, and a knotted rope. When she neared Sugar, she dropped to all fours. "C'mon, Sug, you little scallywag, come play."

My daughter's gifted puppy, the puppy I didn't want before we got her, was a gift to all of us, but especially to me. The way she carried one morsel of kibble from her bowl at a time to eat in the bathroom doorway, the way she listened to me, twitching supple ears. The way she made my sad daughter roll on the dirt giggling. (Three years ago, when Jon had been released from rehab, she'd said, "People are supposed to be sick in the hospital. That's where doctors fix them. But Dad's home now. Why isn't he better?") My original reluctance to get a dog was based on my allergies and anticipation of extra work. But extra chores were worth it and Sugar didn't shed. Sugar gave the daughter of a man with a wounded brain an uncomplicated joy-filled relationship. A relationship that multiplied her confidence.

I swirled another pinch of flakes to the pond, thinking about Wulf, a twenty-eight-year-old vet, the last prisoner I'd volunteered to visit that morning.

He'd run both hands over his bald head before smoothing a coarse red beard that ended at his chest and said his young son's birthday was coming up and he was buying the boy a knife. He expelled a lungful of air. Gifting from prison is hard. "I arranged to get what my youngest wanted for his birthday but now he's changed his mind. That's okay, but it's a lot of work." Shaping his right hand into a pretend phone, he said, "I got my cousin Emmy on the line. She's saying, 'I think this is maybe what you want.' She's describing the knife, and I'm saying, 'Okay, remember what that looks like and now find it on this other website." He threw up his hands. Everything is so expensive for prisoners who earn cents an hour at prison jobs. And Wulf's dad had drained his bank account the moment Wulf was convicted.

Just mouthing his sons' names lit Wulf's freckled face. Made him lean forward on the uncomfortable seat. He felt so

40

tender towards his sons that my body sensed a similar warmth in my own chest. His face had softened last fall when he said, "Talked to my boys on the phone. The little guy wants a computer game for Christmas. I told him I'd buy it and sent Mom the money." He suddenly looked like someone had slapped his cheek. "She used it to buy him a coat."

I mailed my young nephews in Australia science kits that mimicked volcanic eruptions and electric circuitry kits, but I hadn't seen the boys for years and it's hard to maintain long-distance relationships with kids when you can't cuddle or chase them. I missed my nephews terribly but also dreaded the moments when my sister handed them the phone and the silences mounted. I couldn't imagine how Wulf could maintain connections with his sons that might last until he was middle-aged and released from prison.

I trailed my fingers in the pond, listening to Sugar's playful growls and falsetto yips as she and Delia tugged a pink rope. Water mesmerized me — I needed its mirrored reflections and its glimpses of layered galaxies. The breeze rippled its surface and revealed blurred images of Beebop, the kangaroo I'd raised, the canopies of gumtrees exploding in distant bushfires, flocks of rainbow lorikeets. I'd always missed Australia but never so much as after Jon's stroke. Wulf had completed two tours in Iraq, he'd only cried once when he was locked up for forty-five years, his knuckles were permanently red from hundreds of daily push-ups, but he shrank when he whispered, "I can hardly bear to look at their photos. The baby's okay but all I see in Cliff's face is pain."

If I were allowed to give Wulf a gift, it would be to fly his sons to the federal penitentiary in Tucson. But the Bureau of Prison rules forbade me from even sending his family a letter. The only gift I could give was to ask every dumb question I could think of. "What color are Cliff's eyes? How's he doing at school? How do the boys' personalities differ?"

I knelt on the brick paving and lowered my chin to the pond's warm capstones, enjoying the sun on my back. The clustered goldfish hung around for a while, then slowly swam through layers of water, frogspawn, and Brazilian waterweed to the cold at the bottom.

My gift to my husband Jon was to go to marriage counseling even though I mostly hated it. We had long ago exceeded the six annual sessions permitted by our health insurance but somehow, our counselor, Dave, granted us one extension after another. Year after year. Perhaps he saw how honest we were, how hard we tried. And we made progress.

I told Dave that for years, Jon washed the dishes because I cooked, but since the stroke three years ago, he'd gone on strike. He wouldn't relent even when I'd thrusted my peeling hands under his nose. And when I told Jon my eczema couldn't take it, he'd shrugged and walked away. Furious, I'd left the dishes until they stank but was forced to don the yellow plastic gloves when I needed clean knives. Dave stood up, breaking our triangle of three chairs, and grabbed his blue and red markers. He walked to the whiteboard and as he was talking, he drew stick figures of Jon and me, speech bubbles, and arrows. Not for the first time, I was amazed how those diagrams helped me grasp what was going on, helped me understand the core of Jon's resistance. I took a deep breath, staring at the potted plants on the windowsill and the grey sky outside, before turning to Jon. "Look, I know you don't have to do the dishes but will you, please? It's no good for my eczema."

"Thank you." He looked deep into my eyes. "The job of washing the dishes doesn't have my name on it but I agree to do it." Jon's brown hair was as ratty as a floor mop. I wouldn't dare suggest a haircut. He resented me even reminding him to take the meds that saved his life. But at that moment, his ratty hair made me want to kiss him.

Slowly, Dave made me feel that my marriage could be fixed. I still adored Jon. Even when half of his skull had been stored in the bowels of a hospital freezer, when his remaining skull dipped in the middle of his forehead and you could see his brain flop under his scalp if he jerked his head. But it was hard living with a man who scored in the ninety-ninth percentile for some cognitive tasks but who scored in the first for quite a few others. I could deal with the grand mal seizures, or him lighting bonfires at the base of our neighbor's wooden fence. I tried not to scold when he turned on the gas stove and walked away without lighting it, or broke window cranks because he couldn't remember how they worked. It was Jon's diminished emotional sensitivity I struggled with. When we played tug-of-war and he let go of the rope, shooting me to the ground, I had to explain why I cried, had to ask for a hug, even though my leg bled.

It took me a long while to learn that Jon was willing but would only help me if I asked the right questions. Some part of his damaged circuitry made him believe he shouldn't have to give me clues. *Will you help?* didn't cut it. I had to be specific. *Will you take out the rubbish before dinner at six-thirty and wipe the bin clean before putting in a new bag?*

I also learned how to become more transparent. We were sitting by the picture window in the dining room, watching a hummingbird build a thimble-sized nest, when Jon cleared his throat. "I don't want you looking after me anymore."

"What? What do you mean?"

"What do you mean, what do I mean? I can look after myself, thank you very much!"

I squeezed my eyes together hard, squelching an impulse to say, "Well, fuck you!" Instead, I managed, "When you said that, I started to panic. I interpret it in the worst way possible and think you're saying you don't want to be together anymore." It felt so awkward to explain myself. Exhausting.

He touched my arm. "Bean, that's not what I want at all. I just want the chance to try things and fail on my own. I do want you around. You make it feel safe for me to do that."

I blinked back tears. Those tears that come when you think no one has noticed your efforts but then they show you that they have. Even though my efforts felt clumsy. A few times in prison, I'd dug my fingernails in my thumbs, seriously considering falling to the floor in a pretend faint when the men wanted to talk about sports to distract themselves from their suffering, when I didn't even watch the *Olympics*. Jon was never interested in sports, but like the prisoners, he was locked up too—trapped in a new persona and a malfunctioning body. During ten years of marriage, I'd always delighted in his conversations. Post-stroke, I wasn't even sure how to talk with him. But for all my awkwardness, in prison and at home, I was willing to sit in the presence of suffering and keep trying. And Jon was trying, too, trying to perceive the me at the heart of what remains after a bomb.

Benjamin Goluboff
COUPLE-SHTICK

There is, for example, the running bit
about the laundry:
how there is the laundry of color,
the laundry that thinks it is white,
and the laundry that is thermo-atypical.

Or if you say, "Chisholm Trail emotion,"
I know you're talking about
how the Kevin Bacon character feels
in Barry Levinson's *Diner*
when the aristo girl on the horse
tells him her name.

When I speak certain words
that scan dactyl trochee,
like buffalo soldier,
you are likely to holler back
from "Buffalo Soldier."

It is liturgy, freemasonry,
it is Operator's Manual.
On we go through the years.

Elijah Burrell
NEVER SAY *LOVE* IN A POEM

I have been told, and so told
in turn, to not call it "love"
in art but to sell the sense
with things like vision and scent.

Listen: The small of her back
is *drift*, her mouth *supermax*.

If I tell you the soft
beneath her chin is bear paw
jade, you should know
I mean soft and fragrant.

Sometimes I like this unsayable word
to sound like *motorcycle, kickstart* and *snarl,*

to look like leather jacket,
boots. To carry the raisin
scent of an unlit cigarette
before the cherry-burn and smoke.

I felt the thing, just now, with her foot
against mine, and the ceiling fan's

tink-tink-tink above her breathing.

Michelle Menting
QUESTING

When ticks "quest," they crawl to the end of an exposed blade of
grass or branch and extend their legs outward in the hopes that they
can cling on to a passing host. – Seney National Wildlife Refuge

It's true: I do want, and want you.
To be a part of who you are —
your parts to be my parts, all parts
so whole. How lovely is that?

We two become ecosystem
of one. That's hot. Or what
adventure, oh yes, it's a quest
after all, and either one of us

can be hero. You can be
my hero, oh sing it. Or mentor —
all true adventures have one —you,
oh wise two-legged guide, guide me.

You, your parts, become mine,
then mine, so many of my baby
mine. Oh, baby, it's love after all.
Love as connection, as journey.

Such love, hot love, passion.
It's all flow, after all: your flow,
my flow, blood flow. Let me suck
your sweet flow. Let's share,

let's vampire. But it's natural
after all. It's nature: my nature,
your nature, the world outside
with its roots & stems & trees.

Steamy. Lift me up from this blade
of grass, this branch-wick of oak.
I'll reach, I'll reach, I'll reach.

Gian Carla Agbisit
CRISSCROSS

He thinks he is
the rough diamond edges

that make up his sharp tongue
and mind and his time, his time,

stretches like his arm
stretches when he reaches out,

from saltwater beds
and graveyard silence,

and ice cold winter
weather from within.

There is a reason
he loves pullovers, and

wears pushover girls
who, for warmth, would allow

him to pull them in his arms
like blankets, or prayers,

or his other broken pieces.
How could summer be this cold?

The sun is at its noontime height
but isn't shining down on him one bit,

so he chases after sunsets to forget
the tirelessness of the night,

and the night before, and before that.
Maybe he learned this

when he was young:
gasoline meant fire,

friction heats things up, and
when you run a motor for too long

it either buckles or explodes, so
with moth like flap of wings, he

runs his tongue to a dead end speed
crash to burn out

his words, that burns out
his thoughts

so they don't have to stay
while he sleeps. Sometimes

dreams are scarier
than you might think.

In them each night,
he breaks and crumbles too.

And I stay the same
in quiet existence,

inarticulate of social cues
so maybe dreaming

of passive magic, him and I,
standing awkwardly at the dance floor,

hastily groping for words,
finding feelings in weird places,

building mind palaces
in our own snow globe backyards,

imagining broken glass ceilings
under dusty bunk beds,

intricate mind maze sewn
in the underside pockets of musty sweaters,

we carve out happiness
from the awkward

pauses people who just met make,
we are simultaneously bored

and busy with this despair,
so we sidestep each other,

too careful to confront,
too lonely to give it all up.

Kathleen McGookey
EARLY VALENTINE

Snow swirls past my window and settles softly in drifts that cradle the roof, until only a few black shingles peek through. This snow muffles the phone, the blood test, the dishwasher's carcass, dripping. A cardinal lands near the feeder, stark as a heart. A gray squirrel nibbles a slice of red apple it holds in its paws, tail curled like a question mark. Let the snow's hush fill us like the breathing of an old dog, asleep by the fire. All morning, snow falls against the backdrop of more snow.

Mary Jo Firth Gillett
JANUARY SNOW

Already a record month,
sorrow and eight inches more

tomorrow. Smooth-sheened hills
the hue of certain holiday cards

—evening-blue winterscapes
by unremembered artists—

remind us beauty can be harsh.
Sub-zero grates the skin,

no crows caw. See how low
the weighted cedars moan and bend,

life hunkering down,
no tracks in the snow.

Ken Hada
DEER IN SNOW

Gray souls darker than shadows
at dusk follow them
silent as refugees
from one frozen port
to another.

Across white waste
they cut a path
despite a frozen lid
on their world
that confuses
as it obstructs.

Reduced to survival,
life is found in frozen berries
on cedar, pungent twigs,
and stray strands
of empty tall grass.

They move through shadows
too white to be safe,
too white to be feared.

Jim Daniels
TRACKS

A wild turkey scoots through snow
into a thicket of bare, black trees.
For a second, I saw a peacock's colors
in the odd dance of cartoon music.

On a trail in the woods, I add footprints
to the snowy jumble. Memory inflates balloons
into misspellings and inaccurate hearts.
A distant car door slammed the turkey gone.

What happens when electricity's
gone, batteries, matches, candles, gone?
On my desk, a b&w photo: a man
in overalls adjusts an engine, scrutinized

by a slick business suit. The man,
my grandfather, would have been 100
today. A flashbulb burns his shadow
into factory walls now and forever.

For a second, I saw him today tossing
loose change to squirrels — or gold nuggets,
or shards of his pension's worthless promise —
but even below zero, breath was not visible.

Only turkey tracks bruising dusk snow.
He lived to 96, despite scrutiny and shame,
outliving two children, losing his own name
when a policeman took his license for driving

too slow. I wish I had that license.
Gray sky does not relent. We must relent.

Kristy Gledhill

WINTER FAMILIAR

By the distance, the soft howl of memory,
the fields—tilled and blanketed—by the spun
and lofted snow, snaking unsnaking along
the county road, drifting over the tracks, the ditches,

By the sound, scribbled winter wood lots, water towers,
grain elevators miraging in and out of gusts, silenced
and far in the hiss and hush of winter's insistence,
of time's barreling, its linger and longing,

By the hours, the tang of well-water steam, the sweating
kitchen window, its unobstructed view—shifting
over a snowglare mile—of the Ohio line, by the wound buffet
clock, its stiff ticking, its tireless chime,

By the way the pond freezes into a perfect blue-white oval,
by the slumbrous apple trees—Jonathan, Winesap, Snow Apple,
by the shapely Linden, the muffled cistern lid, by the way
nothing happens anymore she hasn't seen,
she knows her home.

Jennifer Burd
DeTour

Five hours due north
and things open out. Sky
gives way to more sky, water
to more water, where Michigan
and Huron meet. The road skims
the blue rim of the lake, shaking
sand out of its empty pockets.
Gulls clutch the last of your fatigue,
dropping the empty shells to the rocks.
The sounds of work – a ferry run,
a hammer, a pickup without a muffler –
mix with mergansers' guttural cries.
Your downstate concerns
are a small sail on the horizon.
Unlike your growing collection
of water-smooth stones, you know
there's no way you can ever take this
back home, nor will you ever fully leave.
Wavelets murmur at your feet.

Jennifer Burd
LES CHENAUX

We take our last trip to the beach –
a strip of sand along the eastern
Upper Peninsula. Our tenderfoot toes
embrace pebble and sedge
like party hosts who try too hard.
Just a short stretch of would-be
dune and we're at water's edge
where the sand is compact and moist.
You watch from the shore as I wade
out to my waist in cold, clear water.
Except that you're not beside me
I don't want to come back –
I've already become lake, become
sparkle, hoisting my thousand
flags of sun.

Betsy Emdin
THE GREAT AUNT

Mom's voice wafted down the basement steps to where I played in the rec room with a Beatles album spinning. I could tell she was talking to Grandma, but something in her voice made me pause from dressing a Barbie. Her voice carried the tone of crisis. I heard great-uncle Norman's name, and that of his wife Lily. Something was wrong.

Lily was Norman's second wife. A prosperous pharmacist, Norman didn't attend church and divorced his first wife. In my family, not going to church every week was almost worse than divorce. We lived in Grand Rapids, Michigan, a conservative and insular place where a standard question upon meeting someone was, "What church do you go to?" But despite his lapses and transgressions, Norman remained a popular family member. We all used his drug store, and he was known to dispense meds without a script to those in need.

No one from the family was invited to the wedding when he'd married Lily a couple of years previous. Norman introduced Lily to the family at the Coffee Gang, an after-church gathering of all my great-aunts, great-uncles, and cousins of varying degrees. They passed around snapshots of the ceremony. Lily wore a red dress covered in white lace. There was headshaking about this nontraditional bridal attire after Norman and Lily left. It was clear this new wife wasn't going to lead Norman back to church.

Lily, who was at least a dozen years younger than Norman, looked like a crooked toothed Liz Taylor with Sophia Loren cleavage. She was a bartender. Grown-ups in the family drank cocktails before dinner, and beer at cookouts, but did not frequent rowdy taverns or mood-lit lounges let alone work in them. Lily's skirts were shorter, hosiery darker, necklines lower, and jewelry bolder than other women in our family. Her makeup was vivid. She had a husky voice. Lily was the only woman in the family to smoke openly—cigarettes that were rimmed with frosty pink lipstick. I thought it was a beautiful color, something that Pattie Boyd might wear. When we visited Norman's drug store, I perused the cosmetics section and admired the pale lipsticks and sky-blue shadows that I saw on magazine covers and on Lily. Colors that I would apply to my face one day when I was allowed to wear makeup. If I was allowed to wear makeup. I wished my mom wore pink lipstick, but she and the other aunts stuck with reddish shades they'd worn since the 1940s and 50s.

Lily had a daughter from a previous relationship, Jeanne, who occasionally babysat for me. I counted her among my favorite caretakers. Norman legally adopted Jeanne, but there were rumors that Lily had never married Jeanne's father. The family regarded this as more scandalous than working in a bar. A naïve ten-year-old, I wondered why that was so terrible. My mom shopped at a grocery store a couple of blocks from a place called the Evangeline Home. It was a place for unwed mothers, and occasionally its pregnant residents wandered the aisles of the store. Mom explained their babies would be given up for adoption. I don't recall it said directly, but I understood there was something shameful about these girls.

Dad returned home after Mom's mysterious phone call with my grandma, and there was more hushed talk. I overheard Lily's name again. What had she done? Did I hear the word "arrested?" No one in our family had ever been arrested. We were so well behaved we didn't even receive parking tickets. This was like a real-life Nancy Drew mystery. I went upstairs to investigate, but they stopped talking when they saw me.

Family members took turns hosting the Coffee Gang. Despite not being churchgoers, Norman and Lily had taken their turn as well. Lily set a lavish table and baked a cake in the shape of a cross one Easter. Maybe it was that day that I heard her say her purpose in life was to help people.

Norman and Lily were not part of the Coffee Gang the Sunday after the phone call, but there were whispers around the table. Talk halted when one of us kids grabbed for a cookie and resumed when we backed away to the other side of the room. All of us cousins wondered what was wrong. There had been hushed conversations in each of our houses, but none of us knew the answer. Norman and Lily did not return to the Coffee Gang again. I missed Jeanne. When we did see them at large gatherings such as weddings and funerals, there was a discomfort with Lily. She was treated with the awkwardness of a barmaid who dared wear a scarlet dress on her wedding day.

I must have heard the word "abortion" in one of the furtive adult conversations. *Abortion*...whispered, followed by a frown. How could I have even known what abortion was at the time when I didn't even know the details of how babies were conceived? How did I learn the bad words? Dirty words. Words that made one gasp. I recall being told the definition of "fuck" by a seventh-grade classmate in the busy hallway of our junior high school. She was a cool girl—the sort who would not usually consort with the likes of me. But she imparted her knowledge without condescension even though I wore undershirts instead of the de rigueur training bras. A few years after that I asked my mother what "solicit for prostitution" meant after hearing it in *The Cross and the Switchblade*, a Christian-themed movie about drug addicts in New York City that was a must-view in my religiously steeped cohort. Mom squirmed while giving a vague answer. But abortion, I don't remember when or how I learned the meaning. We were so good at keeping secrets.

Was Lily involved with abortion? Norman and Lily eventually divorced, but her mysterious transgression was still not talked about. When I was older and my mother was open to frank discussion, Lily was not brought up. But conversations with my mother did include her own conception story. She suspected it was before her parents' marriage. Her mother, my beloved grandma, retained a keen mind well into her nineties, but could not remember her anniversary. I was obsessed with weddings as a child and once asked how old she was when she got married. "Nineteen or twenty," was her reply and she changed the subject. Mom's suspicions were confirmed when we found the marriage license after my grandmother's death. It was dated seven months before her birth. I wonder if Gram, as I called her, with an eighth-grade education and little worldly experience, even knew what was happening when she got pregnant.

Lily, who understood all the facts of life, was out of the family. It was known that she ran a bar in the factory section of town. The legacy of abortion provider trailed her, at least in my mind. I only confirmed it in the age of Google when I dug up a couple of newspaper articles from 1965 naming Lily in an abortion operation. A decade before Roe v. Wade, Lily's sin within our family was as much about breaking the law, committing a crime—a felony—as it was about right-to-life. I remembered her words about helping people.

If the law hadn't changed, Lily might've helped me: me, who eventually learned the facts of life, wore pink lip gloss, and got pregnant. A tryst, a hook-up with an old flame in the front seat of his beat-up old car. I didn't want a baby. I was unsettled, heading to grad school where I was attempting to find myself in the parlance of 1980. I decided on an abortion, a legal abortion, but I wondered about the family history. Where would Lily have taken me? The sketchy newspaper articles didn't provide details. Norman and Lily lived in a well-kept modern ranch house. It was a true ranch on a rural gravel road outside of Grand Rapids, where Norman kept horses. Could it have happened there? Lily was arrested with a co-conspirator—a man whose name I did not recognize. Who performed the procedure? What of Uncle Norman? Did he know? He was never charged, but I thought of the drugs at his disposal. When he died at ninety, more than forty years after this scandal, there were jokes at funeral about his covert distribution of meds. Norman helped people in his way, and Lily in her way.

Instead of Lily, instead of a mysterious location, I walked into a clean clinic near downtown Grand Rapids, accompanied by a close friend—we did that for one another. We weren't harassed, no one thought it their duty to publicly judge us in those less fraught times. I was in a medical suite, upon an obstetrical bed. An OB-GYN did the procedure. He was kind and soft-spoken. The room was cool and antiseptic. A nurse held my hand. I squeezed hers back. She had the touch of an angel. I felt safe. I was safe. Lily would've offered comfort and succor, but I'm glad I didn't have to turn to her.

A few years later, I became pregnant again and was advised by my mother to abort. I celebrate that she, a staunch Christian and churchgoer, was open-minded and pro-choice. Her pro-choice beliefs evolved from my previous pregnancy. But this time I had a graduate degree and a plan. I bore the baby, supported her, and she became a beloved grandchild. No one in the family, other than my mother, knew of my earlier abortion. I was the inheritor of Lily's black-sheep status; I'm sure I was talked about. When my daughter was four, I gave birth to my second daughter. Again, I wasn't married, but lived with this child's dad. We married when she was two months old. A couple of years later, I had my third daughter. When they were of age and ready, I ensured that they had birth control even when it meant dealing with a chilly doctor's office receptionist who clearly didn't approve of the reason I was seeking the appointment. My children are now young women of childbearing age. The oldest has two rambunctious pre-school age daughters of her own.

In 1980, when I walked out of the clinic, and ready to renew my life, I had no reason to believe the laws would ever change, despite maudlin campaigns from right-to-life groups. Years ago, my oldest daughter had a Libertarian professor who believed that Roe v. Wade would not be overturned because it was a carrot to social conservatives to keep them voting for right-wing politicians. I took comfort in that until 2016. That group of voters now know they can get what they want. We're in a world of slamming doors.

I frequently walk my dog past a Planned Parenthood clinic a couple of blocks from my house in Traverse City. They do not perform abortions at this clinic but provide birth control and health services. One of my daughters received low-cost treatment for a condition that had nothing to do with pregnancy. I'm glad that the clinic is there to help people in need. But there are always protesters outside. They carry signs and utter prayers. I've seen groups of uniformed high school students, led by male clergy, chant in front of the building. My dog and I remain on the other side of the street and do not engage with them, but I stiffen and bristle. I'm unnoticed, old, wrinkles furrowing above my mask, slouchy in my Covid wardrobe. I'm the opposite of glamorous Lily.

"I just want to help people," Lily said. She should not have had to do so illegally. If my grandchildren ever hear mysterious conversations, the subject just might be me.

Elijah Burrell
THIS IS THAT SONG
BY ALEX CHILTON ("THIRTEEN")
Elliott Smith Live at Stinkweeds, May 1997

Well it's quiet in here, he says, as he tunes down
and shakes hair from his eyes. Nervous laughter.
You guys doin okay? he says. *Make us cry in our soda,*
someone deadpans. The Yamaha's headstock bounces,
keeps time with his anxious knee — Arizona
silence. *You guys are so quiet, it's freaking me out.*
They've given him a beer to nurse, and a chair,
orange plastic — like for an office — and set him up
beside a box fan and a mini-fridge.
Its fluorescent light pours over the wooden body
of his guitar. *I think Pete has stuff for sale,*
he says, and the whole world stares at their shoes.
When he covers the song, the multi-track harmonies shimmer
through his mind. He closes his eyes. He's back in Portland,
alone in bed, headphones on, and the birch-
white limbs inside him tremble and bend
from the weight of something cold and falling.

Dave Malone
KNOCKING ON DOORS

We were fourteen or fifteen,
the lot of us. Kansas kids
two hours from home
in another beat-up burg.
It was March, after a deep rain
that left the daffodils at attention
like ancient Roman legionaries
and the town huts silver
in the gloaming. Alone,
I hoofed it back to the church
before the other pamphleteers.
Inside, only silence played here
and the smell of a tired air conditioner
battling first heat—such a scent
of surrender, hanging before evening
candles lit.

Patricia Clark
HEART, LATE SUMMER: A STORY

A girl and a boy in a room at a party. Mid-afternoon—still light out, still warm, though the room is dim. New to each other, they lean together and talk. He has a shock of dark straight hair that gleams. She wears a summer dress with small pink flowers.

If there are other people in the room, they leave no impression. It's late summer or maybe school has just started. They are near salt water and his nose, especially, smells it. There's the whine of an outboard motor, and in windows that face the water, a shape blurs past towing a taller shape with a rope.

"Come on," says the boy. "Come for a ride on my motorcycle."

She hesitates. It's her friend Susie's birthday and there's to be a cake, ice cream, the presentation of gifts. This boy, though. The girl studies his face. He's wearing a madras shirt that buttons up the front. She notices his Adam's apple, his throat and neck that disappear into the shirt. His skin browned by the sun.

"Just for a few minutes," she says. "Let's be back for the candles."

Outside, his bike stands shaded under a tree in the yard. The boy has led the girl out by her hand, and her whole body is tingling. The girl does not think she is pretty. How has it happened she is with a boy?

"Did you say your name is Mike?" she asks, and he bends to listen.

"Yeah. I live down near the water."

There's a loud crow above them. *Caw, caw.* The girl has a flicker of doubt. Should she be doing this? She watches the boy straddle the bike, faded jeans, low sneakers. He kicks the engine alive, backs it up, awkwardly, one leg on either side. Leaning one way, then the other. He's not a boy from her school.

"Hop on."

You might think she hesitates here but she knows exactly what to do, never having ridden a motorcycle. She puts a leg over the seat, bunches the dress around her thighs and loops her arms around the boy's waist. The girl looks confident but her stomach twists inside with doubt. She should have told someone they were going. She has never seen this boy before.

Leaning forward, she feels his backbone and warmth through the thin shirt. Dappled light through the trees. Her feet find the pegs to rest on. Beneath them the bike rumbles, a deep throb, a live thing.

The cusp, that's where the girl is, leaving ninth grade for high school, dreaming of what's to come. Her parents know she's at Susie's, but they don't know this boy, or that she is leaving with him. It opens before her: a world where she moves and they don't know her location, her thoughts.

No wonder the air is so bright now, the smell of the sea rich.

Out of the driveway, the boy banks left, follows a curve, and the girl leans with him. She is aware of her breasts under the dress, nerve endings responding to his warmth, his shirt.

A curve to the right now after a stop sign. Ahead of them, the bay glittering aqua and blue, the straight road, Marine View Drive. And he kicks it up, speeding across the blacktop, helmetless both of them, bare arms, and her bare legs.

First they head south, water on their right, sun in his eyes a bit. They turn around in a parking lot at the Cliff House restaurant where some Sunday church people are going in for a late brunch. The girl imagines that the woman in a white hat, blue suit, looks at her with contempt. *Sluttish, really. On a Sunday, too! Riding a motorcycle in a dress.* The girl grips the boy a bit tighter; he heads out again on the road, north this time. Now the wind rushes past, and she has a hard time hearing.

"Seattle," the boy seems to be saying. "Water's edge."

"What?"

"We could go all the way to Seattle this way. Following the water."

The girl closes her eyes, imagining a journey of some hours. She does not know him, and now she doesn't want to leave him. She missed some of his words, she thinks, but it doesn't matter today.

Fir trees, deep shadow when they drive under the trees, and curves, glimpses of the houses below near the water, some with three-car garages, most hidden from view, secret, rich. Again the girl closes her eyes. Is that his heartbeat or her own thrumming there? He seems to be talking again.

"What time is it?"

Her wrist is bare. The sun, that's a clue. "After three?" she offers.

Never has she felt anything like this: the air whisking past, wind in her hair, the sun cooled along her arms and legs by the rushing air, the gasoline smell, the engine, this warmth. She feels she could huddle against him forever. Do they have to go back?

Later, two weeks later, she will think, *Where did the chain and locket come from? Out of his jeans pocket? But how could he have planned this? Was it just to anyone he'd say, "Let's go steady"?* And when the train of thought goes nowhere, she stops. He had pulled it from a pocket. Girl and boy stood under the same tree where they'd climbed onto the bike. Now he said, "Go steady?"—barely a question, shyly asked. And she, without a thought really, barely knowing his name, just thinking of his warmth, his dark hair, the Adam's apple, the throat, his scent of seaweed and smoke, she had said yes.

Back in Susie's house, the dim room, a room with a door that opens out to a flat roof (a deck where people could party and see the bay), someone puts records on, the Beach Boys, everyone's favorite.

The boy says, "Let's dance," and they move together, a slow dance, for the girl the tingling again. The boy is just slightly taller than she is, their bodies match, his leg brushes against hers, for her, sparks.

The song ends, Marie Snyder now— "Let's do the cake." And the boy and the girl, others, crowd near a card table.

"I'll get us some punch," the boy says and steps away.

The girl stands with friends now, Susie blows out candles, laughs, claps her hands. Her red curls shake.

The girl thinks how Susie and Marie and Joyce are longtime friends. She has no one like that.

Joyce steps over, "Did you leave with Mike? Did you learn how to make out?"

The girl looks at Joyce's dark eyes, thinking of the word *piggish*, and wonders *What are the odd words she is saying?*

Now Marie steps in, "Don't listen to her. What's with his finger?"

The girl had noticed his index finger was a stub. Mostly he hid it, tucking it into his hand. He had touched her cheek, though. It had made her flinch.

The boy carries paper cups with the red punch. She feels more shy now in his presence. Still, she almost asks, "What happened to your finger?"

66

"I need your phone number," he whispers. "I'll call you." And he slips the chain into her other hand. "For you —" and with that he is gone.

As though the light goes out. And the girl's father will come at 4:30 to pick her up.

Now Marcia, teasing, loud, "Turnipseed! Turnipseed! That's his name, you know. Yakima kid with half a finger."

"Shut up," the girl says.

"Yakima kid. You going steady? He asks everybody." Marcia's perfect hair swings as she moves her head, laughing. "Did you fall for that?"

It's gone now. The girl waits outside in the driveway. The girl does not know the word *bereft* but hears a low sorrow in the Beach Boys song coming faint through the windows, and she notices a couple of sparrows, dusty looking and brown, trying to sip water from the handle of a garbage can where water had pooled.
Her father pulls up in his black station wagon.

"How was the party?" he says.

"Okay," she says. She looks down at her dress. She remembers how it had been against him, flowers against madras.

The boy calls her one time, a whispered conversation. The girl knows he thinks she is special. He remembers every detail of their ride, just as she does.

No, she cannot meet him.

Yes, she will be at the football game.

The girl knows what is true and also what is wrong. At the game she talks with him under the bleachers where no one can see. Looking up, she glimpses people's shoes and the backs of their legs. Cups and trash gather below on the sparse grass. She wears the pep uniform of her group, the sweater emblazoned with her school name. Now she understands — it rushes back to her — what he'd tried to say that day on the motorcycle. "We could drive all the way to Seattle — This was our nation's homelands along the water." The boy cries when she gives back the chain, and the girl tries not to see it, tries also to ignore her own face, hot, burning up as she walks back to her friends where they sit in a group cheering for the home team.

James Miller
I DIED

I woke up on a pile of folded tables blocking the emergency exit
from a convention hall in the newly renovated Hyatt Regency,
sixteen-storied jewel of downtown St. Louis. The record expo was
over. Vendors were boxing up their vinyl, and hotel staff had rolled
in with a flotilla of vacuum cleaners. I thought I could hear Augustus
Pablo on the PA. Mike Watt came over to help me sit up. I said—
but Mike, you're not dead yet. He reminded me that bass players can
move freely between both worlds. *Look at Richard Davis, man. He spent
six weeks gigging here back in the late 60s, and still breathing all the while.*
By now I was learning to stand again, though I could not walk far.
There were so many questions, but I could only remember one about
Mike on that old Saccharine Trust record. I decided not to ask it.
Yes, he said. *You work here, in the hotel. Changing the sheets, authorizing
electronic keys. Setting up sound.*

Dennis Hinrichsen
["NO REPLY"] [IN STEREO] [WITH SPEAKER WIRE AND AN ACT OF MEMORY]

(left channel)

I am lonely before a photograph of myself@20
which is a kind of stereo when I push at history —
that artificial heart of time that puts chambers in me
and channels in the blood — this me cold and beautiful
and young and blue — singing harmony maybe
the look on the face is so thin — a prescient
pre-existing overdub laying out a future (mine) —
already lived through — breathed through // this me
pressed so close to the mic (that is — *this moment*)
you can hear spit in it — spittle the melody //
— O garage band boy — O oracle of thrash
every gesture you ever made was downstroke — mono —
heap of sound in a box — howl of memory
that utters now — tapes destroyed — not one sound —

(stylus)
so I have to set this
second child
between
us

(right channel)

it's winter — his feet are cold — he has a chocolate cake
under his arm he's won at a school function
so he has *news* — he has a prize to share — but his sisters
make him wait — there's something better — *sound* —
some of it coming from where his mother stands smiling
(there was money — they have spent it — on *them*) —
his father uncoiling speaker wire on the right //
and then Lennon's voice (already helixed in the ear)
gruff — McCartney's almost falsetto accents // how they

69

stand inside that harmony awhile—two minutes
sixteen seconds—listening—and then eat cake //
and now dear boy—family fractured—no one calls—
that box of light you are just a point in time—car ride
with mix tape hissing last empty seconds ending A side

Ann Weil
THE LAST FRONTIER

Today, my son —
a man, no longer my child —
wore a coiled cap
of magnets on his
beautiful, suffering head.

Doctor Cartographer
maps brain regions.
Doctor Scientist
experiments with currents.
Explorers of the interior,
the last great frontier.

Transcranial
magnetic
stimulation.

> *The electromagnet painlessly delivers*
> *a magnetic pulse that stimulates nerve cells*
> *in brain regions involved in mood control*
> *and depression.*

My understanding is a fistful of fog,
a mirror of mist that will not clear.
Like a child, I make up stories
to brush the clouds from my eyes.

Doctor Captain
steers the foundering vessel,
charts in his log
the pull of the tides,
the reach of the moon,
as if willing the forces
to straighten the bent,
right the wrong.

To ease, to ease, to ease.
This, after endless seas
littered with
therapist receipts,
medicine vials,
treatment program brochures,
mother's tears.
A fourteen-year odyssey.
To ease, to ease, to ease.

Hope, a schooner
sailing into the horizon.

Dorene O'Brien
WAITING

The first stab skirts the vein
annoys the nurse, this wielder of tiny swords,
this wearer of bright pink smocks,
this courier of blood red vials.
Perhaps your rebel vein
is keeping her from her Caesar salad,
her midday walk, her lover's call.
She stabs you like she means it,
and you feel sorry for your skin,
say kind things to it, ask its forgiveness.
When your blood crawls
up the small glass tube,
leaving your body forever,
you whisper *goodbye*.

You wait
for the doctor's touch,
for the poke and prod
of disease to take shape
as he talks about his trip to Montana.
Fingers push as he says, "Unseasonably hot,"
thumping and pressing through the ruined hikes,
the dirty water, his furious kids.
You can not feel sorry for him, this man you admire
for the sincerity of his concentration
as he kneads your flesh,
knits his brow while clamping onto something
you're certain should not be there.

Four days, five days, six.
He does not call, this man who was also betrayed by nature,
because he understands the deep root of body rebellion,
because he wishes to give you the gift of not knowing,
for one more day and one more day and one more day,
and so as the murky night descends you touch the place

where his fingers like dowsing rods drew forth
the quickening blackness, the gnawing fear,
your budding certainty.

Cecil Morris
MOTHER AT THE END

The door was open yet she hesitated,
a bird on the sill looking out, looking back,
waiting for weeks and days, still on her bed
and unresponsive, her face losing weight,
flesh receding and bones rising like wrecks
emerging from a drought shrunk lake. Her arms
and legs withered as she lingered and her
stomach continued to swell, the only part
of her still alive, the teeming cancer
relentlessly doubling—the way she made
more cookies appear when we had eaten
the jar to crumbs. Now we brought her ice chips
and damp cloths and the eye dropper of morphine
and daily avowals of love whispered
at her ear along with farewells, kisses
to her forehead, skin there like rice paper,
smooth and dry. We offered her permissions,
as the hospice nurse suggested, blessings,
promises to care for him who did not
seem aware that she was leaving their house,
who kept telling us what they would be doing
once she was well. She just breathed the slightest,
slowest breaths—like a child hiding or feigning
sleep or, finally, in the deepest, deadest
sleep that scared us and made us feel for beat
of heart. Sometimes we thought that she was gone,
that the her of her, the soul, the woman
who always knew our needs and crimes, had left
the body too stubborn to stop for death
but too weak to lift from this life and fly.

Julie Stotz-Ghosh
AN EVER-CHANGING CONSTANT
Moon Cycle: mid-April to mid-May, 2020

Everything is going to be alright, you said.
I balance eggs on the branches of trees.
Pear blossoms make tiny white fists.
I hold your voice in my hands.

I balance eggs on the branches of trees.
The sun is shining — my spirits are high, you said.
I hold your voice in my hands.
On the phone, your voice is soft.

The sun is shining — my spirits are high, you said.
But today there is no answer.
On the phone, your voice was soft.
We run into spring, trailing a monarch-shaped kite.

Today there is no answer.
We hike through dunes.
We run into spring, trailing a monarch-shaped kite.
We skip stones into still water on a great lake.

At the dunes, I ask for an answer.
A white bird circles the clear blue sky.
We skip stones into still water on a great lake.
Suddenly, a white feather at my feet.

A white bird circles the clear blue sky.
It disappears when I look twice.
It leaves a white feather at my feet.
My sons laugh and run down the dune.

I think the moment will disappear if I look twice.
Do we make our own meaning?
My son laughs, holds the full moon in his hand.
I take a picture to keep the moment still.

Do we make our own meaning?
The moon balances on the branch of a tree.
I take a picture to keep the moment still.
It's time for pink magnolias, again.

The moon balances on the branch of a tree.
We bury you beside Mom, beneath the Norway spruce.
It's time for pink magnolias, again.
We place the flowering branches on your graves.

We bury you beside Mom, beneath the Norway spruce.
Magnolia blossoms open, big as my hand.
We place the flowering branches on your graves.
Everything is going to be alright, you said.

Linda McCullough Moore
SHE DID SO LOVE A STEELY SKY

Done with dying, she went home
at daybreak; left so quietly, she
made the world a vacant place;
and now, gray lowering skies,
wind come to rouge my face,
the cold to brisk up pace
and make me thankful
for this afternoon in April,
so very like November.
So unlikely. One sweet,
at the bottom of a winter's tin
I would have sworn was empty.

Romana Iorga

OF ALL THE THINGS I TOOK INTO MY BODY

There is no language without deceit.
Italo Calvino, *Invisible Cities*

i once wrote   on my mother's tongue   i wrote
on it   on the tip   of her tongue   i wrote
    mother   i am afraid   i am afraid of
language   language says things about me   i am afraid
    to read   language says things   that are
not true   but when i read them   mother   i become
    what language says   i read them and forget
myself   that self you carried under   your rib vault
    like an icon   a lighted candle   a prayer
this   is your language   mamă   see?
    she lies to me

                    like this body of prayer
you granted me   language has broken
    all her promises   she has not   given
but taken   has taken   freely   without
    remorse or compunction   compunction
language knows not   what that means   she loves
    words she can hold   on her tongue or
gnash   between her teeth   her teeth
    are shiny   language has teeth   that are
shiny and sharp   tell me   mother   shouldn't
    language   eat   what she wants?   language
does   no matter   your answer   she ate
    you

        language has been so   hungry lately
mother   hungry for yet another   heartbeat
    she moans while   scavenging your grave   she is
what she eats   now i see you   wag your finger at me
    in every careless word   i write   mother   i will

79

never be careless again   mother   i am
     lying to myself   language says   a grave
is your   mother now   language says   you are
     a wanted child   i am ashamed   of her words
mămico   i am   grateful

                                    language has gone
     downriver   language has gone downriver
to drink from the sea   downriver to drink from the sea
     what the sea will grieve   freely   while the sea
takes language in   drinks   language in
     downriver   over cataracts   under a bleached
sun   downriver   where roots are exposed like nerves
     under the crumbling lip   of the ravine   nothing up there
but sky   mother   language has gone downriver
          to drink from the sea that had so much to grieve
when i couldn't

                                    language subscribes to the sea's
     newsletter   seagulls and pelicans   an albatross
now and then   landing heavily   on my shoulders
     language subscribes   to the sea's obituaries
bloated fish   crumbling shore   dried-up seabed
     all of this language takes into   her body   into
my body   mother   i am bursting at the seams   i am
     a window in your torn-down cathedral   i am a memory
of your sky   what was it like to carry me   under that vault
     like a cross   an effigy   an affliction
was i   kneeling   inside your body   mama?   was i
     already   asking to be absolved?

                                    mamă   mămico
of all the things i took   into my body   language
               was the least   forgiving

     80

Dorene O'Brien
TRYING TO END IT

I was dragged into an alley when I was nine by a strange man who snuck up behind me and my 10-year-old sister as we walked to the Catholic school in our dowdy uniforms and winter coats. The man snaked his arm through my legs from behind, grabbing me by my crotch with one hand while wrapping the other around my neck and pulling me backward toward the thin path that ran behind Detroit's tiny bungalows. I didn't scream and I didn't struggle. I didn't understand why the man wanted to take me to that little trail until much later. I had just checked my mittened hand for the nickel I would use to buy a carton of chocolate milk for lunch and I asked my sister if she had hers. For years I would believe that the man had attacked me for my money.

You want to know how this story ends. Of course you do. So do I. But the story never really ends because five decades later I'm still writing about it, trying to end it. I know there was an alley, an overgrown path dark and dank with tangled foliage, I know my yellow boots scudded across the ice toward the end of childhood, and I know the scream that poured from my sister's mouth scared the man away. But I don't remember those things, not really. What I remember is the relief I felt at seeing that glint of silver, that gleaming nickel atop the snow, my nine-year-old self picking it up before continuing that never-ending journey to school.

Sharon Bippus
AMBER ALERT

You are asleep in your bed, your dog snuggled behind your knees. And then, the uncomfortable repetitive drone of the Amber Alert wakes you. Somewhere a child is missing, somewhere a child has been taken. You roll over and look at your phone. Five years old in a light blue snow suit with bunny ears. A white man in a blue truck with Indiana plates. Mikayla Grace, taken from a town sixty miles north of you.

You get up to pee and the dog follows you into the bathroom. You hike up your nightgown and sit in the dark, the dog huddled at your feet, its chin at your lap. You can see in the dark; a bit of moonlight comes in the window. You flush the toilet, wash your hands, and head back to bed.

You like to sleep with the window open. You hear your neighbor, now awake like you, let his dog out. You hear the animal bark. It has picked up on something. A smell, a movement. You imagine the dog pacing alongside the fence wall, sniffing for the scent of a squirrel, a rabbit, or whatever else roams in the night.

You remember when your own dog caught an animal a few weeks ago. The painful high pitched screeching sound you heard and how after calling and calling your dog, it appeared with a strange lifeless creature in its mouth. After coaxing, it dropped the animal at your feet and you saw that it was a possum. You shooed the dog into the house and then turned to tend to the limp carcass. But the animal was no longer there. Puzzled, you scanned the yard to find it now resting, outside the fence, a gash in its belly. A mixture of sadness and hope washed over you. That next morning you looked for the animal, but did not find it. It was gone.

You think about that girl in the bunny suit. Mikayla Grace. You wonder if she is afraid. Maybe she is asleep in that blue truck. Maybe not.

You lie on your side in bed and plump the pillow under your cheek. You adjust the covers, make sure that your feet, your shoulders are underneath the blanket. Your dog returns from his water dish, jumps on the bed, curls at your side. The night is still again. So many times you have been spared, overlooked, unseen, unlike your friends, your neighbors, the crying mother on the news. You have had no terminal illness, no house destroyed by fire, no intruder at your door, no crazed driver in your path.

You think about college and when you didn't have a car, and how you'd often walk home alone, late at night, how you felt at peace then. You kept an eye out for a car that passed you a second time or maybe someone walking behind you. Then you'd duck into a shadow, behind a tree, next to the side of a house, or maybe behind a tall vehicle like a truck or van. And then you'd wait, wait for the stillness to return. You think about that daunting bridge you crossed which had no shadow to hide in, and how you walked as quickly as you could, heart racing just a bit. Still, that anxious tension didn't deter you. You wanted to walk, uncaged in the night, in the darkness.

Years ago your friend Jane was stabbed. Stabbed in the parking lot of her apartment, alone in the night, coming home from a party. Stabbed by someone who was never found. You remember Jane at the hospital, bandaged and groggy after surgery, telling you that her jacket had saved her life. Its layers of thick corduroy had stunted the blade, kept it from jabbing at her kidneys. The jacket had cost three dollars at the Goodwill, and what kind of deal was that?

Whatever happened to Jane? You've lost touch. But when you drive past that hospital, you think of her. Every single time. Left for dead in a parking lot. If somebody else is in the car with you, you don't say anything, but if you are talking, you pause just a moment and take a breath, and then move on with your conversation.

And now, in your bed, you close your eyes and try to still your thoughts, the darkness, all that is unknown, unanswered. In the morning, you will wake, rested, but with no answer for the odd symmetry that is night. And the girl, Mikayla Grace, will still be gone.

T. Clear
PAYNE'S GREY
—a dark blue-grey color used in painting

Not just your eyes, but the nimbus
of clouds behind them. The tempest
embedded there, behind your brow.

And the rain that rumbled after,
settled-in for months.
In the right weather I'd swear

there was nothing but blue
when you flashed a smile,
and laughter spilled from you

bright as godlight from a cloudbreak.
When the mercury sank
and you drunk-stumbled onto the ice,

careless of the snapping crack underfoot —
it was you who slid blue-lipped
to drowning, while I remained

useless onshore, no
hank of rope to toss,
no trick, no last sleight of hand.

Yvonne Stephens
THE BONES OF THINGS I CANNOT FIX
after John Rybicki

Do you know the last time we spoke
was on my deck

through our phones. You were
at home and you were

in your car. Funny thing, how
we could see each other there,

through our phones. Your hair
made more beautiful by the

late summer humidity. All the hair
wanted to do was expand

to meet the touch of your hand
as you moved it from your face

I can never see your beautiful hand
move your strays from your face

no never again, not even through
this phone. And that is something

maybe I'd never say, but I might
write it. I want to fix what happened

even though I know there is ash,
and phones, and cars, and bones of things

I cannot fix.

Sara Maurer
THE WARBLERS

Warblers sing from the pines in Susan's backyard. Their song
is a bell-like crescendo that swells to bursting, then falls apart. I
sit palms-up in a white wicker chair while the sound pours over
me. Each note hits my skin like a fat raindrop landing on the
still surface of a pond, so cool and soft that I want to drive right
back to South Carolina, to the screams of gulls and terns, to the
hammer of ocean waves.

"You would've been a nice touch at the funeral," I say to
them, seeking them in the boughs above my head, but they are
too furtive, too quick. *Funerals*, I correct myself.

"Here we go," Susan says, emerging from the back porch
with two glasses of red wine and a recorked bottle tucked under
her arm. "I hope you like it." But we met in college; she knows
I'll drink anything as long as it contains alcohol. She settles in the
chair next to me. I've come to Hessel, Susan's hometown on the
underside of Michigan's Upper Peninsula, for a getaway. A girls'
weekend. That's what we've decided to call it.

I take a glass from her and raise it.

"To friendship," I say.

"To friendship."

I make myself smile. It feels wooden on my face, heavy
and ill-fitting, so I drink before she notices, filling my mouth
with the sugars of grapes left to freeze on the vine, overripened
cherries, the soft mush of melon flesh, all of it sweet on my
tongue. Too sweet. Even for me. I lower the glass.

Susan closes her eyes and slides out of her flip flops,
flossing her toes with the grass. Sunlight patterns her face. "This
is nice, isn't it?" she asks without opening her eyes. "It's been a
long time since we've been together, just the two of us. How do
you like Hessel?"

"It reminds me of Edisto, actually. Quiet, lots of water,
lots of people out and about."

"Everyone's busy getting ready for the boat show."

This is the pretense for my visit: the antique wooden
boat show, an annual celebration of the useful little vessels that
carried residents from shore to shore for generations. Susan said
the bay used to sparkle with the glint of their mahogany hulls.
Now, it's filled with fiberglass boats that never shrink and never

86

rot. But for this one Saturday every year, the marina bobs again with golden wooden boats: cherished, refurbished, and lovingly coated with glass-like lacquer.

"The only thing I think is strange is that Hessel is surrounded by water, but you never hear it. It's too calm. Back home, the waves are everywhere, beating the beach, erasing everything. Even when you're not listening, you can hear them. There's a static. A constant roar canceling everything out. All I hear here are these damn birds." I wave my arms over my head and the warblers, on cue, produce a fresh deluge of birdsong, so rapid, so pure, it feels heavy.

Susan opens her eyes. "Are you doing okay?"

"I'm fine." I show her the wooden smile to prove it. But then the weight of the birdsong turns the summer air solid and I can't expand my chest. The glass slips from my hand and I drop to my knees to catch it, too late, and the wine seeps into the soil. I want to follow it, cover myself completely, feel the dirt deep in my nostrils and under my fingernails. I rock, holding myself, as deep, earthen moans escape my lips.

"Oh, honey."

Susan folds me in her arms as I writhe, my mouth wide and ugly. I hear the ocean at last, waves pounding against my ears like great brown pelican wings, and then I realize it is Susan. "Shhhh, shhhh, shhhh," she says, holding the cool of her palm against my forehead, my cheek.

Not even a month ago, Michael and I biked the Spanish Mount Trail with the girls. Not even a month ago, Sylvie cried over a lost light-up sandal. Not even a month ago, Celia filled her pockets with rust-colored palmetto seeds. "What are you doing with those?" I asked her. "Growing a palm tree," she said, as though it were already planted, already grown, already giving us shade.

I press the heels of my palms to my eyes. The warblers are silent suddenly, startled by my cries. They watch us from their shrouded perches. I wait, not moving, not speaking, not breathing. Drop by drop, their song trickles into the stillness again.

"I wish Michael and the girls could hear this," I say.

Susan pulls me up from the ground and back into the chair. She sits beside me and refills my glass. The birdsong rains down and we lift our faces to it.

Russell Thorburn
DRINKING WITH JIM HARRISON AT THE HOTEL BAR

It was Harrison at a bar decades ago
who spoke to me about Malcolm Lowry,
his unfinished novel high on our list
for reading that winter but who reads
that mad genius today other than alcoholics
or poets wanting a close look inside.
To be alone is to be alive, Harrison said,
inferring that to get inside the soul
as it was called you had to pick desolate
places of snow or shine. His grisly face
of a one-eyed Inuit sage was overburdened
by death, that coin which was flipped
up in the air many times to see if he'd live
or die when it landed: heads or tails.
Whenever we looked outside at the snow,
an eyelid of his appeared to twitch,
veins widened in his vast forehead.
He ordered one vodka after another
at the hotel bar where I was a night porter
not exactly on the job or doing anything,
the two of us suddenly throwing back drinks.
I was working to support three sons and wife,
our house of over one hundred years.
If I told Harrison this, I don't know,
and after so many drinks, I'd be on
the black list for working there without
the enthusiasm of somebody on his way
to the scaffold: that noose Harrison
knew in his Yesenin letters. Everybody
got fired at the hotel. I was one. But only
a few got to meet with Harrison whose
way of talking was a kind of percussion.
You never heard such beats of resolute silences,

his mind among the dragonflies and mosquitoes
where he'd sing of a girl with freckles
and eyes like a sky that seemed to last forever
as long as he kept talking, as long as he kept moving
toward something he knew would never be there again.

Dan Gerber
THE LOST HOUSE

> *See each thing in this entire world*
> *as a moment of time.*
> —Dogen 1233

The one sobering apparition
that greeted our return each June,

half a mile up the beach —we
were never quite sure how far—

half-collapsed and clinging
to a cliff in the shadows

of three enshrouding pines
whose roots seemed all that held

the surviving structure in place after
the sand dune on which it sat

surrendered to years of pounding storms and
the rising level of Lake Michigan.

The brown of the the shakes and
the interior shadows had further

darkened with soaking and rot
in the gloom of the pines,

with several limbs grown
through spaces where windows

looked out, no longer
a structure separate from the trees.

It would have been easy to imagine
the house as a shipwreck pitched

up on the cliff in a horrendous storm
or as a morbid doll house, cut away

to expose the life inside, or
where the life had been, and

there *was* life — Cliff swallows
fashioned their gourd-like

nests along the eaves and
the yellow, Mud Dauber wasps that

stung like 'tarnation,' we were told,
and once I saw a fox with three

kits close by and wondered if she
had her den in there, and

wondered about the people who
seemed to have simply

fled the wreckage that had
been their aerie on the

vastness of the lake
with the silhouettes of ore

boats and freighters,
back-lit Xanadu's taking for-

ever across the horizon.

There were dares
to climb up into the

cave of the derelict house
and the story of boy who

died in there, in a very strange
way. I thought, bled out from a

wound just right of his right eye,
hurling rocks and loosened bricks

at crumbling wallboard when
one missile bounced back, they figured,

right into his temple, though
no one I knew remembered his name.

And summers later, we
returned to find the haunted wreckage gone,

the receding cliff all bare white sand,
with a few clumps of couch grass

and in the lapping of the lake on the beach
below, the amphibious body of one ancient pine.

Between storms the great lake
rises and falls, unnoticed,

like breath if you aren't
paying attention, as the clock

continues, whether or not you
think of time. The silent ships passing.

On calm days you might believe,
with only a little determination

you could walk out to one of those
ships and be one of the deckhands,

leaning on the taffrail, gazing
back at the distant shore.

All the summers we told our friends
the legends of the house, the little

we knew and the more we
heard, from year to year, and then

the summer we couldn't
be quite sure where

the house had ever been.

CONTRIBUTOR BIOS

GIAN CARLA AGBISIT is currently a student of Comparative Aesthetics at the Université de Picardie Jules Verne, France. She is also a Philosophy instructor at the University of Santo Tomas, Philippines. Some of her poetry and short stories can be found in *Aji Magazine* and *Elevation Review*, among others.

LORELEI BACHT (she/they) is running out of ways to define herself, and would like to reside in tranquil uncertainty for a while. Recent work appears in *Anti-Heroin Chic, Visitant, The Wondrous Real, Abridged, Odd Magazine, Postscript, PROEM, SWWIM, Strukturriss*, and *Hecate*. Instagram @lorelei.bacht.writer and Twitter @bachtlorelei.

*SCOTT BEAL is the author of *Wait 'Til You Have Real Problems* (Dzanc Books, 2014) and *The Octopus* (Gertrude Press, 2016). He teaches writing at the University of Michigan, serves as Dzanc Writer-in-Residence at Ann Arbor Open School, and co-hosts the monthly Skazat! reading series in Ann Arbor.

*SHARON BIPPUS's stories have appeared in *The Bear River Review, The Jellyfish Review, The Pinch, The MacGuffin, 3288 Review, Lullwater Review* and elsewhere. She is a former special education teacher and now devotes her creative energies to writing. She lives in rural southwest Michigan.

DEBORAH BURAND is a professor of clinical law at NYU School of Law where she directs the International Transactions Clinic and co-directs the Grunin Center for Law and Social Entrepreneurship. When not teaching, she's writing a nature memoir about making legacies in surprising places, even if that means moving dumpsters.

*JENNIFER BURD is author of two full-length books of poetry, *Days Late Blue* and *Body and Echo*. She is also author of a book of creative nonfiction, *Daily Bread: A Portrait of Homeless Men & Women of Lenawee County, Michigan*. Her newest book, *Fringe*, will be published in 2023.

ELIJAH BURRELL is the author of *The Skin of The River* (2014) and *TROUBLER* (2018), both by Aldrich Press. His writing has appeared in *AGNI, North American Review, The Hopkins Review, Southwest Review, The Rumpus*, and elsewhere. He teaches creative writing and literature at Lincoln University in Jefferson City, Missouri.

*PATRICIA CLARK is the author of *Self-Portrait with a Million Dollars*, her sixth book of poetry. Recent work appears in *Plume, Paterson Literary Review, Tar River Poetry, The Westchester Review*, and *Midwest Quarterly*.

Seattle poet T. CLEAR's poetry has appeared in many magazines, including *Crannog, Sheila-na-Gig, The American Journal of Poetry*, terrain.org, and *The Moth*. Her book, *A House, Undone*, is the 2021 winner of the Sally Albiso Award from MoonPath Press. She is an Associate Editor at *Bracken Magazine*.

HEATHER COUSINS lives in Madison, Georgia. She has degrees from Bryn Mawr College, Johns Hopkins University, and the University of Georgia. She has been published in such journals as the *Chicago Review, Pleiades*, and *Cave Wall*. Her chapbook *Freeze* (2013), published by Codhill, was inspired by her childhood in Michigan.

*JIM DANIELS's latest poetry book is *Gun/Shy*. Other recent books include his fiction collection, *The Perp Walk*, and his anthology, *RESPECT: The Poetry of Detroit Music* (2020), co-edited with M. L. Liebler. A native of Detroit, he lives in Pittsburgh and teaches in the Alma College low-residency MFA program.

LENNY DELLAROCCA is founding editor and co-publisher of *South Florida Poetry Journal* (SoFloPoJo) www.southfloridapoetryjournal.com. His work is forthcoming in *Cimarron Review* and *Slipstream*. His publications include poems in *Nimrod* and *Seattle Review*. He has four collections under his belt and is working on a fifth simply called *E*.

*BETSY EMDIN grew up in Grand Rapids, raised her family in Holland, MI, and lives in Traverse City. She has a MFA in Creative Nonfiction from Goucher College. Her work has appeared in radio program *This American Life, the New York Times, The Sun, The Christian Science Monitor*, and *Midwest Living*.

DINA FOLGIA is an MFA candidate at Virginia Commonwealth University. She won a 2021 Penrose Poetry Prize honorable mention, and a 2020 AWP Intro Journals Project nomination. Her work appears in *Ninth Letter, Stonecoast Review, Defunkt Magazine*, and *Kissing Dynamite Poetry*. She is a poetry editor for *Storm Cellar*. Twitter: @dinafolgia.

*LINDA NEMEC FOSTER is author of twelve collections of poetry including *The Lake Michigan Mermaid*, a 2019 Michigan Notable Book (with Anne-Marie Oomen and Meridith Ridl) and *The Blue Divide*. A collection of prose poems, *Bone Country*, is coming in 2023. Foster is the inaugural Poet Laureate of Grand Rapids.

*JOY GAINES-FREIDLER's third book, *Capture Theory*, is a Foreword Review Finalist, and an Edward Hoffer Award Finalist. Her chapbook *Stone on Your Stone* co-won the 2021 Celery City Chapbook Contest. Her work has appeared in *The MacGuffin, Panopoly*, and *Rattle*. Joy teaches creative writing for non-profits and communities at risk.

*DAN GERBER's tenth poetry collection, *The End of Michelangelo*, will be published this fall by Copper Canyon Press. He's published three novels, two volumes of nonfiction, and a short story collection. He lives with his wife and their menagerie, both domestic and wild, in the mountains of California's central coast.

*MARY JO FIRTH GILLETT's collection, *Soluble Fish*, won the Crab Orchard First Book Poetry Award. She's published four prize-winning chapbooks and poems in *The Southern Review, New Ohio Review, Bayou, Southern Poetry Review, Poetry Daily*, and *Verse Daily*. She's won the N.Y. Open Voice Award and a Kresge Fellowship.

*KRISTY GLEDHILL writes from the unceded Puyallup land colonially known as Gig Harbor, Washington, pining for her Michigan home from a place she loves. Of all the things she brought west with her 27 years ago, her keen eye for spotting Petoskeys has proven to be the most useless.

BENJAMIN GOLUBOFF is the author of *Ho Chi Minh: A Speculative Life in Verse* and *Biking Englewood: An Essay on the White Gaze*, both from Urban Farmhouse Press. Goluboff teaches English and Environmental Studies at Lake Forest College.

KEN HADA's recent book, *Contour Feathers* (Turning Plow Press 2021), received the Oklahoma Book Award. A professor at East Central University, he is the author of ten collections and directs the annual Scissortail Creative Writing Festival. More at: kenhada.org

GILLIAN HAINES lives in the Sonoran Desert and volunteers teaching inmates creative writing. Her work has been nominated for the Pushcart Prize. Read the men's work in the *Rain Shadow Review*, and more of Gillian's in *The Tishman Review, Bridge Eight, Biostories, The Cherry Tree*, and the *Santa Clara Review*.

JOSEPH HARDY, a reformed human resource consultant, lives with his wife in Nashville, Tennessee. His work has been published in: *Appalachian Review, Cold Mountain Review, Inlandia, Plainsongs*, and *Poet Lore*. He is the author of a book of poetry, *The Only Light Coming In* (Bambaz Press 2020).

*DENNIS HINRICHSEN's most recent work is *Schema Geometrica*, winner of The Wishing Jewel prize from Green Linden Press. His tenth book, *Flesh-plastique*, will appear in 2023. New poems appear in *The Cincinnati Review, Ninth Letter, Posit, RHINO* and *Witness*. He served as the inaugural Poet Laureate of Lansing 2017-2019.

RICHARD HOFFMAN has published memoir, short fiction and four volumes of poetry. *Gold Star Road* won the Barrow Street Press Poetry Prize and *Noon until Night* won the Massachusetts Book Award. He is Emeritus Writer in Residence at Emerson College, and nonfiction editor at *Solstice: A Magazine of Diverse Voices*.

Originally from Chisinau, Moldova, ROMANA IORGA is the author of two poetry collections in Romanian. Her work in English has appeared or is forthcoming in various journals, including the *New England Review, Salamander, The Nation*, as well as on her poetry blog at clayandbranches.com.

*ELIZABETH KERLIKOWSKE is a native Michigander. Her new chapbook, *The Vaudeville Horse*, will be out from Etchings Press in June. Her work has recently appeared in *Sleet, Calyx, Book of Matches* and other publications with cool names.

*STEPHEN LEGGETT grew up in Manistee on the shores of Lake Michigan, a region with a geography of snow, wind, and waves that has continually informed his writing. His most recent chapbook of poetry, *For All Things in Motion*, was published by Alice Greene & Co. in December 2021.

*JEANNE BLUM LESINSKI, co-author with RANDY PRAAY, writes nonfiction, flash fiction and poetry. Her recent work has appeared in *Non-Binary Review*, the Alphanumeric podcast, *F3LL, Midway Journal*, and *Plainsongs*.

*ELLEN LORD is a Northern Michigan native. Her writing appears in *Walloon Review, R.k.v.r.y Quarterly Journal, U. P. Reader*, and Poetry Society of Michigan anthologies. She won the Landmark Books Haiku Contest in 2017 and 2019. She is a member of Freshwater Poets and Charlevoices writer's groups.

DAVE MALONE is a poet and writer from the Missouri Ozarks. His latest poetry volume is *Tornado Drill* (Aldrich Press, 2022), and he has poems forthcoming in *Delta Poetry Review* and *Midwest Zen*.

*SARA MAURER lives in Sault Ste. Marie. She completed the Stanford Continuing Studies Certificate in Novel Writing in March. Her first novel, also set in Sault Ste. Marie, is in the works.

*KAZ MCCUE is a visual artist, educator, curator, and arts administrator. He teaches visual arts at the Leelanau School and serves as Artistic Director for Michigan Legacy Art Park. His work graces the cover of this issue of *Dunes Review*. See more at https://kaz.art2xs.com.

*KATHLEEN MCGOOKEY has published four books of prose poems and three chapbooks, most recently *Instructions for My Imposter* (Press 53) and *Nineteen Letters* (BatCat Press). She has also published *We'll See* (Parlor Press), translations of French poet Georges Godeau's prose poems. She lives in Middleville, Michigan with her family.

MICHELLE MENTING teaches poetry and creative writing at the University of Southern Maine. Recent poems and flash pieces appear or are forthcoming in *Cincinnati Review, EcoTheo Review, About Place, Passages North, Radar Poetry, SWWIM*, and others. Originally from the Great Lakes, she lives along a small river in rural Maine.

*TODD MERCER's short collection, *Ingenue*, was a winner of the Celery City contest. His digital chapbook, *Life-wish Maintenance,* is available free at Right Hand Pointing. His poem "Overextended" won a Dyer-Ives Poetry Prize in 2022. Recent work appears in *Literally Stories, MacQueen's Quinterly*, and *Spartan*.

JAMES MILLER (he/him) is a native of the Texas Gulf Coast. He is published in *Best Small Fictions 2021* (Sonder Press) and in the *Marvelous Verses* anthology (Daily Drunk Press). Follow on Twitter @AndrewM1621. Website: jamesmillerpoetry.com.

LINDA MCCULLOUGH MOORE is winner of the Pushcart Prize. Her work endorsed by Alice Munro, she frequently hears from readers who write to say her work makes a difference in their lives. She has mentored award-winning writers of fiction, poetry, and memoir. She is completing a collection of her poetry.

CECIL MORRIS writes his poetry mainly in California, where he lives with an indulgent partner, the mother of their children. He has had poems in *2River View, Cobalt Review, Ekphrastic Review, Evening Street Review, English Journal, Hole in the Head Review, Midwest Quarterly*, and other literary magazines.

*NORA NEILL lives in a historic home in Kalamazoo, Michigan with her wife, daughter, and at least a couple of cats. You can find her writing in *Midwestern Gothic, So Glad They Told Me*, and *Plainsongs*.

*DORENE O'BRIEN was awarded the Red Rock Review Mark Twain Award, the Chicago Tribune Nelson Algren Award, and the Bridport Prize. She is an NEA, a VSC, and a Hemingway-Pfeiffer writing fellow. *What It Might Feel Like to Hope,* her second book, won an Independent Publishers 2019 Book Awards gold medal.

*RANDY PRAAY is a guitarist and storyteller who grew up hunting and fishing in Saginaw, Michigan. He worked with co-author JEANNE BLUM LESINSKI for his piece in this issue.

LitHub named *ALISON SWAN's fifth book, *A Fine Canopy*, one of eleven most anticipated 2020 poetry releases. *Fresh Water: Women Writing on the Great Lakes*, is a Michigan Notable Book. For her work to protect the Saugatuck Dunes, she received a Mesa Refuge writer's residency and the Petoskey Prize for Environmental Leadership.

WILL STIEFEL is a fiction writer and brand storyteller originally from New Jersey. He lives and works in Brunswick, Maine.

*RUSSELL THORBURN is a playwright and author of *Somewhere We'll Leave the World*. An NEA fellow and first poet laureate of Michigan's Upper Peninsula, he lives in Marquette with his wife. His poems appear in *Respect: The Poetry of Detroit Music* and *Undocumented: Great Lakes Poet Laureates on Social Justice*.

*ANN WEIL writes at the corner of Stratford and Avon in Ann Arbor, Michigan, and at Snipe's Point Sandbar off Key West, Florida. Her poems appear in *Crab Creek Review*, *Whale Road Review*, *Shooter Literary Magazine*, *Indianapolis Review*, and elsewhere. See more of her work at www.annweilpoetry.com.

*ELLEN WELCKER is the author of *Ram Hands* (Scablands Books, 2016), *The Botanical Garden* (Astrophil Press, 2010) and four chapbooks, including *The Pink Tablet* (Fact-Simile Editions, 2018). She lives in Traverse City, MI.

READER BIOS

*KELLI FITZPATRICK is an author and editor from Michigan. Her fiction has been published by Simon and Schuster, *Flash Fiction Online*, and *Crazy 8 Press*, among others, and her poetry appears in *Dunes Review*, *Still Life*, and *KYSO Flash*. She has written and edited for the *Star Trek Adventures* game line from Modiphius. She is an advocate for the arts, public education, and gender rights and representation. Connect at KelliFitzpatrick.com and on Twitter @KelliFitzWrites.

*CHRISTOPHER GIROUX received his doctorate from Wayne State University and is a professor of English at Saginaw Valley State University, where he has served as faculty advisor for the school's literary magazine and co-founded the community arts journal *Still Life*. His second chapbook, *Sheltered in Place*, is scheduled to be published in 2022.

*PAUL OH is an aspiring writer. He recently received his undergraduate degree in Creative Writing from Colorado College. Paul's currently splitting his attention between too many projects, across various forms of poetry, fiction, and essay writing.

*TERESA SCOLLON's recent publications include the poetry collection *Trees and Other Creatures* (Alice Greene) and an essay in *Elemental*, an anthology of Michigan essayists (Wayne State University Press). A National Endowment for the Arts fellow, she teaches the Writers Studio program at North Ed Career Tech in Traverse City.

When *EMMA SMITH was in middle school, teachers said she was having difficulty reading. As her worried parents contemplated purchasing Hooked on Phonics, Emma picked up *IT* by Stephen King and hasn't slowed down since. She loves to read everything from sci fi/fantasy to outdated anarchist literature to the classics. You can find Emma working with animals, reading books, or hiking with friends.

*JENNIFER YEATTS' literary life has included MA and MFA degrees in poetry, teaching writing in various forms, and editorial roles at *Passages North* and *Fugue*. She is the director of coffee for Higher Grounds Trading Company.

*denotes Michigan native or resident

SUBMISSION GUIDELINES

Dunes Review welcomes work from writers, artists, and photographers at all stages of their careers living anywhere in the world, though we particularly love featuring writers with ties to Michigan and the Midwest. We are open to all styles and aesthetics, but please read the following paragraph carefully to dive a little deeper into what we're looking for.

Ultimately, we're looking for work that draws us in from the very first line: with image, with sound, with sense, with lack of sense. We're looking for writing that makes us *feel* and bowls us over, lifts us up, and takes us places we've never been to show us ordinary things in ways we've never seen them. We're looking for poems and stories and essays that teach us how to read them and pull us back to their beginnings as soon as we've read their final lines. We're looking for things we can't wait to read again, things we can't wait to share with the nearest person who will listen. Send us your best work. We'll give it our best attention.

Submissions are accepted only via our Submittable platform: www.dunesreview.submittable.com. We do not consider work sent through postal mail or email. Any submissions sent through email will not be read or responded to. Please see further guidelines posted on our site. We look forward to reading your work!

Call for Patrons

Dunes Review is a not-for-profit endeavor to promote creative work within the Northern Michigan writing community and beyond.

The cost of publication can be underwritten in part by individual contributions. We invite you to support the publication of the next issue with a donation of $25.

Send your check payable to **Michigan Writers** to:

Michigan Writers

P.O. Box 2355

Traverse City, MI 49685

Thank you in advance for your support!

CPSIA information can be obtained
at www.ICGtesting.com
Printed in the USA
JSHW020911280722
28580JS00004B/14

9 781950 744091